Jackie Brown MSc, MCSP, DHP.

As well as being a qualified hypnotherapist, Jackie Brown has over 35 years' experience as a physiotherapist and 25 years' experience as an acupuncture practitioner. Jackie has dedicated the past ten years of her career to helping couples suffering with fertility issues. She has given several talks to local hospitals and at acupuncture and physiotherapy conferences on treating fertility problems and was delighted to speak at the Infertility Network UK meeting in Cardiff in 2014. Jackie has clinics in CRGW and in Cardiff.

Is Your Mind Fertility Friendly?

Don't let your emotions hijack your fertility!

Jackie Brown

Matador
9 Priory Business Park,
Wistow Road, Kibworth Beauchamp,
Leicestershire. LE8 0RX
Tel: 0116 279 2299
Email: books@troubador.co.uk
Web: www.troubador.co.uk/matador
Twitter: @matadorbooks

ISBN 978 1784624 644

British Library Cataloguing in Publication Data.
A catalogue record for this book is available from the British Library.

Typeset in 11pt Bembo by Troubador Publishing Ltd, Leicester, UK

Matador is an imprint of Troubador Publishing Ltd

In memory of my parents, Mary and Brian Williams
For Marcus, Chris, Lauren, Helen and Richard
For my patients past and present — you are all an inspiration

Contents

Introduction

If you are reading this book it is likely that you (or someone very close to you) are starting to think about having a baby. Some of you may already be experiencing some fertility issues and may be finding it difficult to become pregnant. You may have tried everything there is – Clomid, IUI and even one or more cycles of IVF or ICSI.

Or for others among you, perhaps you have only recently started to try for a baby and would like to prepare yourself in every possible way for the journey ahead. Perhaps some of you already have a child and can't understand why you aren't getting pregnant as quickly the second time around. Whichever stage you're at it seems as though everyone around you is pregnant.

This book is designed to help you with the emotional aspects of trying for a baby; to help you understand the emotions that accompany fertility treatment, should you need it, and to help you gain confidence in yourself and in your body. It is designed to help you regain control, particularly if you have been trying for some time; to help you improve your general health physically and emotionally, and to help you really prepare for that much-wanted pregnancy and healthy baby. So many of my patients prepare for the financial and social adjustments that accompany a pregnancy but they forget to prepare their mind and body for the challenges ahead in order to give themselves the best possible chance of conceiving and going on to have a healthy pregnancy.

The aim of this book is to help stop the downward spiral of

emotions that affects so many women when they are trying for a baby. When you don't become pregnant month after month the despair and hopelessness and frustration can consume every part of you and eat into every aspect of your life. Becoming aware of this and actually taking note of the way you're feeling and the way you're thinking is actually half the battle. By learning to take a day at a time and focusing on each and every moment, you will stop your mind running away from you like an express train. Practising mindfulness, meditation and some of the other techniques described in this book, may help to stop you falling into that trap of despair. Frustration, anger, anxiety and impatience are all negative emotions that will only compound the problem; being able to let go and learning to recognise your feelings, and having the strength and ability to change them, will change the way you see and deal with your problems. Doing this is empowering and you then feel that you are in control. It is a practical approach, but it will help you get through this period of your life positively and optimistically.

Most women grow up believing they will have a baby when they decide the time is right for them, and those words 'when the time is right' are actually quite important! It then becomes quite a shock when things don't happen the way you've planned them. That is why I believe it is important to understand your emotions before they impact on your fertility, and that's why I chose to write this book.

I believe that prevention is better than cure, and I hope that by following the recommendations I have set out you will achieve your dream of becoming a mum. Eating the right foods, doing a moderate amount of exercise and practising the relaxation techniques will all contribute to helping you achieve your goal. Thinking positively and practising imagery and visualisation techniques will also encourage new neuronal pathways to form in your brain (neurogenesis). Lighten up, laugh and have fun, and don't put your life on hold — so many women postpone holidays and decline wedding invitations 'just in case' they're pregnant. Life goes on and you're more likely to conceive when you're least thinking about it. Control your inner voice and stop the worrying and ruminating by practising mindfulness techniques which allow you to focus on the present moment. Be thankful and think about all the people and things around you that you're grateful for – appreciate what you already have in your life instead of fretting about the things you don't have. And above all, have a belief in yourself and your body and know that one day very soon, yes, you will become a mum.

All of the case studies in this book are genuine patients that I have seen over the years. Nearly all have had acupuncture or hypnotherapy or a combination of both as well as being encouraged to practise some self-help techniques on their own. I hope that this book will encourage you to use the self-help techniques, and that you will be able to address your emotional issues on your own without having to go to the expense of acupuncture, hypnotherapy or other complementary therapies. However they are there and widely available should you need to use them, and of course are excellent in helping you with stress relief.

I hope you find this book uplifting, and that it gives you the reassurance you need and helps you to understand why managing your emotions is crucial to fertility; but above all I hope it helps you to overcome your fertility health issues.

The first step is to understand why some people have fertility issues, what the terms fertility, infertility or subfertility really mean, and what it does to your body and your mind as you embark on fertility treatment. Knowledge is power and the knowledge and information you gain from reading this book will give you a much greater understanding of any hidden issues that may be impeding your chances of having a baby.

Chapter One

Oh, what a power is motherhood, possessing a potent spell.
All women alike fight fiercely for a child.
(Euripides, *Iphigenia in Aulis*, c. 405 BC)[1]

Relax and It Will Just Happen!

'Relax and it will just happen!' How many times have you heard this from well-meaning family and friends? All you want to do is shoot them! Because in reality you are not stressed and you don't feel stressed. You are angry that people even think you might be stressed. Yes, you may be very busy, juggling work with the myriad of other things in your life, but you don't feel stressed or out of control.

You may however be experiencing some other emotions such as frustration, worry, fear, anger, anxiety, grief, jealousy, envy, disbelief, or you may even feel resentful towards another person.

You may also have some other health issues such as IBS or migraine, or perhaps you frequently catch colds. Maybe your menstrual cycle is irregular or inconsistent, or perhaps your periods are very painful with heavy blood loss or clotting. What you probably don't realise is that a normal and regular cycle is essential to conceiving, and that your emotions can actually create havoc with your hormones, interfere with your cycle and hijack your fertility without you even realising it!

1

What is Infertility?

The World Health Organisation (WHO) has defined infertility as a disease of the reproductive system, and by the inability to achieve a clinical pregnancy after one year or more of regular unprotected intercourse.[2]

Infertility is one of the fastest growing areas of medicine, alongside obesity, diabetes and depression. Is this testimony to 21st century living? It is estimated that a total of five million babies have been born worldwide with the help of fertility treatment.[3] IVF clinics all over the country are bursting at the seams with 180,000 babies born in the UK every year as a result of IVF. Roughly £500 million is spent on fertility treatment every year in the UK alone![3]

It was an enormous leap in reproductive medicine when Louise Brown, the first IVF or test-tube baby, was born in 1978 as a result of the pioneering work of Robert Edwards and Patrick Steptoe. Since then the speciality has grown from strength to strength with the development of ICSI (intra-cytoplasmic sperm injection), whereby a single sperm can be injected directly into the egg. The main advantage of this is that even with very few sperm fertilisation is still possible.

IVF was originally developed for those women with either blocked or no fallopian tubes, but most would agree that a large proportion of couples now seeking IVF are those with 'unexplained' infertility. 52% of IVF cycles in the UK in 2013 were due to male factor infertility, whilst 42% were due to unexplained infertility. Of these 41% were funded by the NHS, and 58.7% were privately funded. Two thirds of women undergoing IVF were under the age of 37 years![4]

It is estimated that there are 70 million couples worldwide experiencing fertility problems, with several million diagnosed with unexplained infertility.[2] Unexplained infertility refers to cases in which medical science has not found a cause or a reason for the infertility. According to research eight out of ten couples who seek medical advice either do not start or fail to continue with fertility treatment, the main reasons for this being the low success rates and the cost both financially and emotionally.[2]

Women face so many problems associated with fertility and these include:

- Unexplained infertility
- PCOS
- Endometriosis
- High FSH
- Low AMH
- Amenorrhoea
- Male factor infertility – low sperm count, poor morphology, poor motility etc.
- Undertaking assisted reproduction techniques – IUI, IVF and ICSI
- Age
- Miscarriage
- Secondary infertility

Unexplained Infertility

According to the WHO, infertility is a disease of the reproductive system. Is infertility really a disease of the reproduction system, or are there other factors involved? What about the couples diagnosed with unexplained infertility – is that still a disease of the reproductive system, even though medical science has not been able to find an actual problem causing the infertility? In other words, if the reproductive organs are not diseased then what is causing the problem? If there is no physiological reason for the infertility then should we be looking elsewhere for the answers? Do the answers lie hidden beneath the turmoil of emotions caused by the struggle to conceive? Can the mind-body relationship really affect the ability to conceive?

Are fertility problems a condition of our time? Is infertility a disease of the 21st century? One thing is sure – fertility problems are on the increase. In the 'good old days' families were large, with ten to twelve children being the norm. Granted, there was no contraception to speak of, and certainly no contraceptive pill interfering with our hormones! Also lifestyles were so different with the majority of women working within the home; there was one car per household if you were lucky enough to afford it but most people walked, cycled or used public transport. Household chores were more physically taxing – there was certainly no need to rush off to the gym at the end of the day! Food was usually grown and reared locally as well as being homemade – there was no convenience food in those days, bursting with additives and preservatives! And of course there was very little in the way of technology; people were not bombarded with phone calls, text messages, emails and all the social media networks that we have today. The television (if you were lucky enough to have one at all – these days there appears to be one in every room!) finished after the *News at Ten* – there was no 24 hours of available television with a vast selection of channels, and no Sky+ to record programmes that you didn't have time to watch! Altogether, life was lived at a much slower pace, and was quite frankly much simpler! Less choice meant less stress.

Compare that with today's living – everyone is busier than ever; in fact it's almost fashionable to be busier and more hectic than ever before. Is stress the new addiction? We are in a perpetual state of hurry, hurry, hurry. Is this so-called busy, competitive lifestyle interfering with our ability to conceive? After all we know that high blood pressure, high cholesterol, heart disease, irritable bowel syndrome (IBS) and some skin complaints are just some of the conditions that can be attributed to a busy and stressful lifestyle. If that's the case then can the same be said of infertility? The medical community have bandied this question about for years and are still unable to agree! However the evidence linking stress with infertility is becoming more compelling, with several studies published in the last decade. There is in fact a wealth of information showing that what goes on in the mind can have an adverse effect on hormone levels, ovulation and other reproductive factors such as implantation. A study published in March 2014 concluded that women who were stressed took twice as long to conceive as those who were not stressed.[5] In this study they recruited 501 couples and asked the female partners to collect their saliva immediately on waking in the morning. 401 women (80%) completed the study from 2005–2009. When someone is under stress, the hypothalamus springs into action and adrenaline is released into the bloodstream, which eventually results in an increase in the hormone alpha-amylase in the saliva. It was this salivary alpha-amylase that was measured. The women that had the highest levels of alpha-amylase had a 29% decreased chance of pregnancy and took longer to conceive when compared with women with the lowest levels of salivary alpha-amylase. The researchers also concluded that there was a greater than twofold increase in risk of infertility among those women. The study went on to say that *stress reduction modalities, such as yoga, meditation and mindfulness, that have been shown to be helpful in reducing stress in studies of other health outcomes, might be relevant for further consideration.*

An earlier study by Professor Sarah Berga from Emory University, Atlanta, Georgia looked at a small group of women in their 20s and 30s who had not had a menstrual period for six months. She found that all the women had increased blood levels of cortisol, which is linked to stress. However the strange thing is that none of the women complained that they were stressed – they all said that everything was fine. Stress had become the norm for these women; it had become a way of life and they didn't notice it anymore! Professor Berga went on to say that *maybe these women have unrealistic attitudes about themselves and think that they can get more done in a day than is realistic and that their sense of worth depends on achievement.* Half of the 16 women in the study received cognitive behavioural therapy (CBT) and the other half had no treatment. Twenty weeks later they found that 80% of the CBT group had started ovulating again, with two of the women becoming pregnant two months later.

There have been numerous other studies supporting the theory of the link between the mind and body in cases of infertility. The Psychosomatic Infertility Study in 1994 showed a remarkable 65% success rate in women who became pregnant and went on to have full-term pregnancies after having nine sessions of hypnotherapy.[6] These women had averaged three and a half years of infertility prior to taking part in the study. A study based at Harvard Medical School by Dr Alice Domar and published in *Fertility and Sterility* studied 184 women who had been unable to conceive for one to two years. The women were divided into two groups and one group received a mind/body programme while the other group did not. The women in the mind/body programme had a 55% pregnancy rate compared with 20% in the other group. Dr Domar, who is a pioneer in the field of mind/body fertility, has published numerous studies and is the author of several books on the subject. She states that *Infertility can be enormously stressful; research has shown that the stress levels of infertile women are equivalent to women with cancer, AIDS, or heart disease. Conversely, recent research from around the world has shown that the more distress a woman reports prior to infertility treatment, the less likely she is to conceive. Thus, in order to both improve the quality of her life, as well as to optimize the chances of treatment success, mind/body techniques are an excellent complement to standard infertility treatment.*[7]

The hypothalamus controls both stress and the functioning of our reproductive system and so it is not surprising to find a link between the two. Stress has a negative impact on fertility.

When a woman fails to conceive month after month her stress levels increase, creating a downward spiral that is difficult to get out of. But why is stress such a taboo subject when it comes to infertility? We know that stress is a real condition and can cause so many other health issues, and that people get medical treatment for stress, but when it comes to infertility everyone seems to tiptoe around the subject. If only stress could be diagnosed, accepted and treated early on, particularly in cases of unexplained infertility, I'm convinced it could save thousands of couples years of heartache and distress, not to mention the cost of fertility treatments.

One of my patients with unexplained infertility decided to go straight for IVF, in her words *because there is absolutely nothing wrong with either of us, we thought we'd go straight to IVF*. Why, then, with perfect 'textbook grade' embryos and an endometrial lining that is triple-lined, did the IVF simply not work? This patient was only able to attend two sessions with me due to long working hours. She also had some other health issues, complaining of migraines, disturbed sleep and some digestive problems – surely this in itself is a clue to the fact that she was under a great deal of stress? Had she had the time and inclination to attend a few more treatment and relaxation sessions maybe I could have addressed her issues. Most fertility clinics, although they provide some form of counselling, don't actually address the mind and body fertility connection.

According to Dr Bruce Lipton, a cell biologist, *Stress is the root of all illness and that 95% of all illness and disease is linked to stress.*

★

Patient 2

When I first saw this pleasant health care worker she had been trying to conceive for two years. She was on the waiting list for a laparoscopy and dye test to check the patency of her fallopian tubes. She had been diagnosed with unexplained infertility up until that point. Her past medical history showed that she had had shingles twice and also complained of some IBS-type symptoms. She was self-employed running her own business, was very busy and worked long hours, often until 8pm. On top of that, she also taught part-time at the local university. Her menstrual cycle was regular, with a heavy, clotty flow. The main issue was the terrible pain that accompanied it – often making her feel sick and leading her to almost pass out with pain. She had been prescribed mefenamic acid (also known as ponstan) which is a non-steroidal anti-inflammatory drug used for menstrual pain.

I first saw this patient on day 12 of her cycle and the following week on day 18, when she complained of a headache after the acupuncture treatment. The following week she came in looking exhausted and very pale. She said she had had a terrible stomach bug all week, with sickness and diarrhoea. When I saw her two weeks later she said that it hadn't been a stomach bug at all, but that she was pregnant. We continued with treatment throughout her pregnancy and she went on to have a healthy baby boy and delivered him at home.

Patient's Story

Diolch yn fawr – thank you – Go raibh mile maith agat! In all three languages the words don't seem enough to say how grateful we are for the gift of our beautiful son. After two years of trying to conceive, with all the tests coming back as negative, it was looking likely that we would need fertility treatment to help us conceive a child. And then someone I knew told me about you and the rest, as they say, is history! After just one session I fell pregnant. I carried on having regular sessions with you throughout the entire pregnancy to keep my body balanced and highly recommend doing so to everyone. It was my one hour for myself to relax, let the needles do their thing and practise my hypnotherapy. As my due date approached we discussed using different points as a pre-birth treatment and to prepare my body for labour. Our gorgeous son arrived on time as planned without any medical intervention at all. We just used the TENS machine, acupressure, hypnobirthing and the birthing pool – all at home. Even the midwives said they had never seen such a calm and relaxed labour and delivery. So 'thank you' seems totally inadequate – but THANK YOU!

★

PCOS

Polycystic Ovarian Syndrome (PCOS) is one of the biggest causes of anovulatory infertility in women. It is thought to affect around 6–10% of all women and the symptoms include:

- Irregular or non-existent menstrual cycles
- Weight gain, obesity or difficulty losing weight
- Excess body or facial hair
- Acne or poor skin
- Hormonal imbalance with increased levels of testosterone
- Difficulty in getting pregnant

★

Patient 3

I remember this next patient clearly, largely because she wasn't your typical PCOS patient, but also because of the way she responded to treatment. She was tall and slim and although she didn't have the weight issues or the facial hair that accompany so many women suffering from PCOS, the scan of her ovaries did show that there were multiple cysts and the classic 'string of pearls' appearance. She had not had a period for several months. It was October when I saw her and her last period had been in January. She responded brilliantly to treatment and had a period at the end of October and again in November, but then missed December's. She was delighted to have had two periods and her lack of a December period she said was 'normal' for her. Imagine her delight when she found out she was pregnant! She had a wonderful pregnancy and gave birth to healthy baby boy.

Patient's Story

> *At last I have some time to get in touch with you and to say a big 'thank you' for helping us to become the proud parents of our gorgeous son. We didn't ever think it would happen naturally with my non-existent periods. So thank you so much for everything.*

★

PCOS is a complicated health issue and if you are struggling with it you will have realised that the abnormal cascade of hormones produced by PCOS also triggers the release of additional stress hormones. These stress hormones in turn trigger further metabolic disturbances and may lead to even more weight gain, fluctuating mood swings and fatigue.

All the self-help techniques discussed in this book will help you to cope with and live a life with PCOS. There are tips on nutrition and exercise. Getting out and walking or starting any form of physical activity is going to boost your mood and feelings of wellbeing, as physical activity improves the function of body and mind. Also, exercise is an essential part of the management of PCOS as it can not only help you burn more calories but it actually decreases your appetite too! It doesn't have to be all or nothing when it comes to exercise as I found out. Even if you only have a few minutes to spare it's worth it. I love cycling, but went through a busy phase while writing this book and thought that if I didn't have time to cycle for two or three hours at a time it wasn't worth doing! How wrong I was – just going out for 20–30 minutes was enough to make me feel good. It reduced my stress levels, gave my endorphins a boost and made me realise how easy it is to just waste time procrastinating about doing something but then not doing it because you don't think you have the time! Just go out and just do it!

There is evidence now to suggest that exercise in short 'bite-size' episodes of three ten-minute sessions throughout the day is just as effective as doing a straight 30 minutes. Anything is better than nothing at all and you will be amazed at how much better you feel. Even if you can only manage walking for ten minutes three times a day, it soon adds up and is definitely worth doing. Walking stimulates your metabolism and helps to build muscle and burn fat. More activity builds more muscle and muscles burn more calories than fat does. It's an excellent way for women with PCOS to get moving.

Endometriosis

Endometriosis is a common gynaecological problem affecting millions of women worldwide. It happens when endometrial tissue is found outside the womb and in the pelvis. This endometrial tissue responds just like the womb lining and bleeds during menstruation. However, because there is nowhere for the blood to go it bleeds into the pelvic cavity and causes adhesions and scarring. It is associated with infertility because the adhesions and scarring can be a mechanical obstacle to conception, either by stopping the fallopian tubes from moving to catch an egg as it is released from the ovary, or sometimes because the scar tissue is actually wrapped around the ovary itself. There may be some immune issues associated with endometriosis because it is classed as an autoimmune condition, and there may also be an inflammatory component as well.

Endometriosis can only be accurately diagnosed by a laparoscopy, where a tiny camera is inserted into the abdomen. Endometriosis is thought to have an inflammatory component, but what scientists are not sure of is whether the inflammation is the cause of endometriosis or a result of it.

★

Patient 4: Ectopic Pregnancy and Endometriosis

This patient had been trying to conceive for two and a half years. She had conceived naturally the previous year, but sadly it ended in an ectopic pregnancy and she ended up having surgery to remove the fallopian tube. During the surgery they also found that she had endometriosis, with several adhesions and a cyst on the opposite ovary. She was advised to have IVF and was put on the waiting list, although there was a chance that she could conceive naturally. Her other past medical history included shingles and viral meningitis two years previously, and she suffered from hay fever and other allergies.

When I saw her she was exhausted and run down and had started to have panic attacks. When she came to see me she said that while waiting for her IVF she wanted to improve her general health. She wanted to feel calmer and less stressed and also wanted help with hormonal balance as she felt her hormones were 'all over the place'.

We started with acupuncture and then after a couple of sessions we discussed adding some relaxation and hypnotherapy, including some visualisations. This patient was worried that as her good ovary was on the opposite side to the remaining fallopian tube she would never conceive without IVF, so we visualised that fallopian tube waving around, searching to catch the egg at the appropriate time in her cycle. We also visualised a healthy ovary and a thick and luscious womb lining.

After five months of acupuncture and hypnotherapy the patient decided that she would like a break from trying, and from the treatment. Unbeknown to us both she had actually conceived that month. When she realised a couple of weeks later she returned for treatment and continued to have sessions throughout her pregnancy as it helped to keep her calm and relaxed. She gave birth to a healthy baby boy in the summer, and I've recently heard from a colleague of hers that she's conceived again – naturally!

★

Endometriosis can affect women in so many ways. There is often excruciating period pain, not to mention heavy bleeding every month. Sometimes there is spotting or bleeding between periods. Fatigue can often result from being anaemic, and feelings of depression, anxiety and low self-esteem can also be felt, not to mention the stress and despair of not being able to conceive.

Endometriosis is probably one of the most challenging conditions to have in women's health; not only because of the pain involved but also because it can seriously affect your self-image and your relationship. It can affect you emotionally as well as decreasing your fertility, and even your ability to work if the symptoms are severe enough that you have to take sick leave. All of these can leave you feeling frustrated, helpless and out of control. However, it doesn't have to be like this. By recognising that you have this condition you are on the right path to taking control, and by taking control you will feel more positive and less helpless. The self-help techniques discussed later in this book will help you to take back control and you will feel empowered both physically and mentally as you adopt the mind and body techniques to help you cope with and manage your endometriosis.

High FSH

FSH or follicle stimulating hormone is measured on days one to three of the menstrual cycle. Many IVF clinics still use this test to determine a woman's suitability for IVF. A reading higher than ten generally means that many clinics consider the woman unsuitable for IVF unless she can bring her FSH level down to ten or under. Their argument is that with a high level of FSH the ovaries won't respond to the medication in the same way and as a result very few if any follicles will be produced.

FSH is normally secreted by the pituitary gland, in response to a message from the hypothalamus to signal the ovaries to produce follicles. If the ovaries don't respond, and no follicles are being produced, the pituitary tries harder and so produces more FSH to 'persuade' the ovaries to respond. Higher levels of FSH indicate how stubborn the ovaries are.

This however does not have to be a marker for the woman's level of fertility. The hypothalamus, which signals the pituitary to produce hormones and is considered the 'control centre' for reproduction, is also highly sensitive to stress! So when a woman is feeling stressed that then upsets the hypothalamus, which in turn upsets the pituitary and the balance of hormones required for ovulation. The result is a high FSH level, disruption to ovulation and a diagnosis of infertility. Remove the stress and technically everything returns to normal!

An AMH or anti-Mullerian hormone test is a test that determines how many antral or dormant follicles there are left in the ovaries. A low AMH does not necessarily mean that you will not be able to conceive. Often in fertility clinics an AMH test is done alongside the FSH test in order to assess how much medication will be required to stimulate that woman's ovaries as she goes through an IVF cycle. If the FSH is high and the AMH is low the woman will invariably be told that she is in early menopause and the only solution will be IVF with donor eggs. This is because a low AMH means that ovarian stimulation with IVF drugs will be difficult and so they recommend using donor eggs. This will of course send the poor woman into a complete frenzy, because this is the last thing she wants to hear.

*

Patient 5

This was exactly the case with one of my patients who was diagnosed with an FSH of 76 and an AMH of below one. She was only 31 at the time and I can remember the first day she came to see me accompanied by her mum. Both were inconsolable as they had only recently received the diagnosis of high FSH and low AMH, and had been told she was in premature ovarian failure. She had been recommended to come and see me by a friend of a friend. Eventually after they had calmed down and we had gone through a few strategies (including reminding her that there is no rush at all if she was going to have donor eggs as they are not ageing!), I suggested that I get her back on track physically and emotionally and to take things from there. We looked at lifestyle and diet and relaxation techniques, and we started acupuncture and hypnotherapy as a combined treatment, which actually works very well. Even I was taken by surprise when after five weeks she came in and burst into tears again, saying she was pregnant! She went on to deliver a beautiful baby girl and not only that, when her daughter was only five months old she discovered she was pregnant again – this time with a healthy baby boy.

★

A low AMH level does not necessarily mean you won't conceive naturally, but it does make it more difficult to stimulate the ovaries with IVF drugs, which is why clinics recommend using a donor.

Amenorrhoea

This is when the woman is not ovulating and not having periods. PCOS is the biggest cause of amenorrhoea in women. It can be caused by others factors, e.g. post-contraceptive pill amenorrhoea, which is when the periods don't return after stopping the pill, or it can be caused by stress. Other factors that can lead to an absence of periods include excessive weight loss or excessive weight gain, or indeed over-exercising. As well as being a factor in lack of menstruation, stress can also be responsible for the emotional disorders that can contribute to weight loss or gain.

If your periods have stopped or you have never had any then it is advisable to see your GP immediately as well as practising some of the self-help techniques explained in the book.

★

Patient 6

This pleasant teacher came to see me for help with anxiety and a very irregular/almost non-existent menstrual cycle. Her job was very stressful and she'd had an eating disorder in the past.

She responded very quickly to treatment and became pregnant in the first month despite not having a period, and went on to have a healthy baby boy. When it was time for a second she came back as once again her cycles had become very irregular after breastfeeding. This time it took a few months before she fell pregnant and after a non-eventful pregnancy gave birth to a beautiful little girl.

It was when her daughter was just over a year old and just about to finish breastfeeding that she got in touch again as she wanted a third child. Lo and behold, soon another baby was on the way – we couldn't believe it!

Patient's Story

A friend recommended I see Jackie as I was very run down at the time, and my cycle was all over the place. I could go for months and months without a period. Although we were in no rush to start a family, I wanted to have the option. I was very stressed and the acupuncture just calmed me down completely and I would fall asleep on the couch. I have no doubt that the stress relief and relaxation brought about by the acupuncture contributed massively to my conceiving all three of my children.

*

Male Factor Infertility

Male infertility, like female infertility, contributes to almost 40% of fertility problems and in the remaining 20% of the cases it is the combination of both partners that cause the failure to conceive. This suggests that men and women are both equally responsible for fertility issues.

Stress affects men too and it is not unusual to find that if a couple have been trying for some time, the male partner's sperm has decreased over that time. Physiological and psychological stress can also affect male fertility, and research shows that stress can adversely affect the morphology (or normal shape) of the sperm. A study in Boston in 1999 showed that increasing stress levels led to a decrease in sperm quality.[8]

It is difficult for men when they see their partners struggle with infertility. Quite often they feel helpless and sometimes even left out, as they try to support them as much as possible through this stressful time. They often don't know what to do to help, and feel they have to be strong and supportive, but a lot of the time they may have feelings of guilt if the problem is on their side. They may be doing everything they can to help such as decreasing consumption of alcohol, tobacco and caffeine, while at the same time trying to increase their consumption of fruit, vegetables, nuts and seeds.

Most often however men don't know how to, or simply can't, address their emotions. Sometimes men will perceive emotional disturbances as a weakness and so will try to suppress them in order to appear strong and competent on the outside. The self-help techniques described in this book will be of huge benefit to the guys too; in fact there may be relaxation activities that you can practise together such as walking, meditation or yoga.

It's also frustrating for the female partner when there is male factor infertility, particularly if they believe their partner is not doing everything in their power to change things. I have only come across a few couples where the man is adamant he's not giving up his 'boys' night out', or won't stop smoking or doesn't like vegetables. This can result in a lot of stress and tension between couples which are not conducive to fertility, particularly if the couple are going through an IVF cycle.

Most men are committed to doing everything possible and will change their lifestyle accordingly, and are more than happy to do everything in their power to help as they can't bear to see their wives emotionally distraught and want to be as supportive as possible.

★

Patient 7: Low AMH and Husband Decreased Motility

This 36-year-old lady came to see me having been diagnosed with a fairly low AMH, but her husband also had decreased motility (slow-moving sperm). She had undergone two ICSI cycles, the first of which had been successful but sadly ended in miscarriage at eight weeks. The second cycle was negative.

Her past medical history showed that she suffered from migraines, had IBS and complained of stress and tiredness. She had been prescribed sertraline for clinical depression. She was preparing for her third ICSI attempt and wanted to try acupuncture and hypnotherapy to help her through it as she was feeling very anxious and quite negative. She was also concerned about her weight as her BMI was 35.

Her menstrual cycle was regular, with a dark flow, and she passed clots. She also had pain on the first two days. She was not sleeping well and had taken some time off work to try and ease the stress.

She conceived naturally before her ICSI planning appointment and was absolutely delighted. I continued to support her throughout the first trimester as she was understandably quite anxious and afraid of having another miscarriage. She also suffered from morning sickness, which improved with acupuncture, rest and frequent small meals. The rest of her pregnancy was uneventful and she gave birth at full term to a healthy baby boy.

★

Assisted Reproduction: Clomid, IUI, IVF or ICSI

You may be having assisted reproduction for a number of reasons, but whatever the reason think of it as a positive next step on your journey to motherhood.

The majority of women grow up believing that they will have a baby when they decide the time is right for them. Up until that point most women are focusing, ironically, on how to prevent themselves getting pregnant. It then becomes quite a shock when things don't happen the way they think it will. Although most people have heard of others going through IUI or IVF they don't expect to be one of them.

All of the self-help and stress management tips in this book are just as beneficial if you are undergoing assisted reproduction treatment (ART), whether it is Clomid, IUI, IVF or ICSI. Research has shown that women who were anxious about undergoing IVF produced 20% fewer eggs and had a 19% reduced chance of fertilisation than those who were less stressed.

If you are undergoing ART, it may be a decision that you haven't made lightly, or perhaps it is the only option for you and your partner. Whatever the reason it is to be embraced. The enormous advancement that has been made in medical science today has meant that thousands of couples are helped every year by techniques such as IUI, IVF or ICSI. So although you may be feeling apprehensive about IVF, think positively – it is giving you another chance to have that much-wanted baby.

Clomid or Clomifene Citrate

This is the first line in fertility treatment and is often prescribed for unexplained infertility or for women who have difficulty ovulating, such as those with PCOS. Clomid is designed to stimulate ovulation and can also be used in IUI. It is taken on days two to six of the menstrual cycle. When used in women with PCOS it is often prescribed in conjunction with metformin.

IUI (Intra-Uterine Insemination)

Many women, when they decide to have assisted reproduction therapy, will start with IUI. It involves inserting sperm high into the womb at the time of ovulation, to give the sperm the best chance of getting into the fallopian tubes ready to meet an egg, allowing for fertilisation to take place naturally. Most women have a fertility drug to stimulate their ovaries to increase the chance of producing a follicle. Usually the woman is given a trigger injection 36 hours before to stimulate ovulation. IUI is suitable for most cases of infertility except where there are blocked or no fallopian tubes, or where there are inadequate or slow-moving sperm. Many couples opt for IUI initially as it is less costly than IVF, is less invasive and does not have the emotional strain that IVF has. It's often a gentle introduction to the more sophisticated IVF.

IVF (including ICSI)

IVF doesn't have to be the emotional rollercoaster that so many people say it is. Most women will approach IVF with mixed feelings – some will be excited and thrilled that medical science has been able to overcome issues that would otherwise have rendered them childless. Other women are fearful because they don't like needles, or are not used to taking any medication, let alone having it injected into them. Some women may be anxious in case it doesn't work, while others are angry because they didn't want to go down this road in the first place. At the end of the day, it is what it is – try not to resist it but go with the flow, taking one step at a time through each stage of treatment.

An IVF cycle consists of many stages of treatment and each stage brings with it emotional peaks and troughs. For many women IVF eventually starts after they've been trying naturally for one or two years. Then there may have been three to six months of Clomid, followed by one to three IUI attempts. Some people may have been on an NHS waiting list for 12 months or more. All of this amounts to several years of anxiety, stress, frustration and childlessness. For some couples if they can afford to pay privately they may decide to go straight in at the deep end just as this patient did:

Because there was nothing wrong with either of us, we decided we didn't want to wait and so decided to go straight for IVF. We thought IVF was bound to work – it never occurred to us that it wouldn't work because there was nothing wrong with either of us and now we don't know where to go next. I just find the whole thing so frustrating.

Before IVF starts there is the anticipation and the anxiety and the waiting. Maybe waiting for your period to start so you can have your baseline scan, or perhaps you are on an NHS waiting list, waiting for that all-important letter or phone call to say that you've reached the top of the list. During this time, as hard as it is, do try to remain as positive and calm as possible.

By following my suggestions in the fertility programme before you embark on your IVF journey you are giving yourself the best chance of success by making sure you are as fit and healthy as possible. This is true for the guys as well. It is definitely worth doing because you are putting so much at stake that it makes sense to be as healthy as possible before you start.

By doing this you can use the time waiting for IVF to focus on something positive, and you will feel pleased that you are doing something that is in your control. Many women feel helpless and so doing something helpful alongside their treatment can help them feel more positive. So many of the aspects of IVF are out of your control – you are told when to do the injections, when to have the scans etc. – that it is nice to be able to do things that you are in control of. I think this is why so many women enjoy coming for acupuncture or hypnotherapy: they choose to attend and they also have some control over the appointment times. They feel like they are regaining some control; they feel that they are doing something positive and they don't feel so helpless.

There are so many stages of IVF:

- Treatment planning appointment
- Down-regulation starts on day 21 of your cycle (long protocol)
- Menstruation starts
- Baseline scan to check that the uterine lining is thin
- Stimulation of the ovaries with injectable drugs to produce a large number of eggs
- Series of scans to check the ovaries' response and also the womb lining
- Egg collection
- Eggs placed with the sperm
- The embryologist monitors (or aids, as in ICSI) the fertilisation of the eggs and their development into embryos
- Decision whether to transfer the embryos at three or five days
- Day of transfer
- The two-week wait!
- Any remaining high-quality embryos will be frozen for future use

Each of the above stages of IVF brings with it different levels of stress, worry and anxiety.

I think the hardest period for my patients is the two-week wait and it is quite normal to feel excited one minute and then down in the dumps the next. Many women worry about abdominal cramping, while others worry if they don't have cramping. I always tell my patients not to look too hard for signs that may or may not be there as quite often the medication may be causing or masking things anyway. Nausea, breast tenderness, tiredness and going to the loo more frequently are all signs that women look for. I try to encourage my patients to think about the positive aspects of their cycle; the fact that they had so many eggs, the fact that they were fertilised and so on. I do think visualisation helps – to visualise the embryo implanting and flourishing in the womb, although some women find it incredibly hard to do this.

The most important thing is to take one day at a time, practise the relaxation and breathing techniques mentioned later on in the book, and to become mindful – focusing on today and not what might or might not be in two weeks' time. Don't worry about things that are out of your control.

Some people find it helpful to practise gratitude. Think about the people supporting you through this cycle – your partner, your family, your friends and the medical staff. Be grateful for their help and support, be grateful for getting this far in your cycle, be grateful for the chance to experience such a medical miracle that many years ago women like you did not have, be grateful for having the funds to pay for IVF and so on.

Some women find it so difficult to allow themselves to think positively; to think that the treatment might work is almost too much to bear because they want it to work so much. They hold themselves back as they believe they will have further to fall if they think positively and then it doesn't work. Personally I think if you have done everything you can including thinking positively, then whatever happens you can take heart that you did everything in your power to help.

In my experience, people who do take it one step at a time manage to cope more easily with the whole process, and they appear less stressed and more in control. Focusing on the positive things you are doing will help you feel better instead of thinking about the negatives, e.g. 'I wish I'd had more eggs.'

After all, it only takes one, as I said to one of my patients who was in tears because she only had one embryo. When she came for acupuncture pre- and post-embryo transfer, we focused on that one embryo, how strong and special it was to have survived. We focused on it implanting and she also did lots of visualisation – seeing it nestling into the luscious womb lining. When she text me two weeks later to say she was pregnant we were both ecstatic. In a further phone call a few weeks later she told me that the first scan had showed two tiny heartbeats – that one embryo had divided into two! She went on to have a healthy pregnancy and gave birth to two beautiful baby girls – all from that one embryo. It only takes one! It just goes to show!

Age

People make incorrect assumptions about you – wanting a career, not wanting kids, but wanting exotic holidays. All I have ever wanted is to be a mum.

Women are encouraged to go to university to get a degree and to have a good career, and yet we are criticised for being 'career-minded' and leaving it too late to start a family. We just can't win.

There is so much in the media these days about age and fertility that many of my patients are entering their 30s already terrified or anxious that they won't be able to conceive, even before they've started to try. I do believe, and of course this is just my opinion, that the media and the medical establishment are partly responsible for creating anxiety and fear amongst women wanting to conceive in their 30s and 40s, and this only serves to increase the problem! Because women are told they will struggle to conceive later in life, this is what they believe and expect and of course this is what happens!

Women over the age of 35 are worried that when they do get pregnant it will be fraught with complications and genetic defects, which is not entirely true. It is possible to get pregnant in a reasonable time and to give birth to a healthy baby up until about the age of 40. According to Dr Elizabeth Muir, *psychological and emotional factors, not age, have much more influence on a woman's chance of conceiving.*[9]

Obviously fertility is going to decline as we get older because women will have had more periods and used up more eggs. Research has also shown that the risk of miscarriage is higher in older women, but this is what you have to remember: as Christopher Williams said, *for the vast majority of women who have delayed child bearing through no fault of their own, everything will be OK.*[10] You have to remember that!

Also what we have to remember is that our life expectancy has increased massively over the last decades, and recent studies in America have found that having a child in your 40s actually increases your chances of living to a hundred years of age by more than four times. This is probably due to a more active lifestyle. Additionally, a consultant paediatrician in London says that the parenting skills of the older mum are more positive, and that the children of older mothers are less likely to become ill or have to attend hospital.

Women having children into their 40s is not a new thing because before any form of birth control it was assumed that women would go on having children right through their fertile years until they reached the menopause, and they did!

Here is a letter from one of my more mature patients:

Dear Jackie,
    Enclosed as promised is a photo of our beautiful baby boy. It is amazing to think that this time last year

I was in the middle of my acupuncture sessions with you and hardly daring to believe that this day would ever come. I remember being particularly down on Mothers' Day last year having recently lost my own mother, and wondering whether I would ever become a mum myself at the ripe old age of 42! It was a joy to celebrate Mothers' Day yesterday and I would like to thank you, not only for your treatments but for your real empathy and belief in what you have to offer.

Of course my husband is taking most of the credit for our beautiful son! But my sessions with you helped me to feel positive, healthy, balanced and relaxed throughout what is a most stressful time.

With heartfelt thanks again…

Looking after yourself can also help significantly and research has shown that stimulants such as smoking and alcohol have been linked with an early menopause, while caffeine has been linked to miscarriage. So by adopting a healthy lifestyle you can actually help reduce the risk.

In his book *Perfect Health*, Deepak Chopra mentions some research that showed that people who practised regular meditation were biologically younger than their actual age. Some of them were as many as 12 years younger than their chronological age because the longer they had been meditating the 'younger' they became![11] Further research showed that meditation could actually increase the levels of the hormone DHEA in the body[12] and we all know that DHEA is important in fertility, so much so that some fertility clinics actually prescribe it, particularly to their older potential mums, to improve egg quality. So start meditating – the sooner the better – and it will help you in more ways than one!

One of the biggest issues I have come across when it comes to age and fertility is that couples believe they have to conceive quickly before their time runs out. As a result they are impatient to conceive in the first month or two. This of course only adds to the anxiety and frustration and in actual fact will add to the delay.

The other crucial point of course is whether you know the best time to have sex. I have been surprised how many of my patients of all ages have no idea when the most fertile time of the month is! So many assume it's *after* day 14! How wrong could they be? According to research the best time is two days *before* ovulation – so if you have a 28-day cycle ovulation will be around day 14 and so the best time for sex is two days before that – i.e. day 12 – allowing the sperm time to travel up into the fallopian tubes and be ready and waiting to catch the egg. In a 26-day cycle intercourse should be around day ten, and in a 35-day cycle ovulation will be around day 21 and so intercourse should be around day 19.

I remember many years ago myself and an old colleague were 'trying' around the same time. I had a 28-day cycle and was fortunate to conceive quickly; my colleague however still hadn't several months later. I then remembered that when we worked together her cycle had been longer than mine and I reminded her of her 35-day cycle and tentatively asked on which days of the month had they been trying? She of course said day 14, and as sperm can only survive for up to five or six days they wouldn't have been around for her ovulation on day 21! The minute they changed the days they had intercourse she conceived straight away.

I also think that the older you get, the less sex people have which again is going to have a bearing on how quickly you get pregnant, especially if it is the *wrong* side of ovulation!

So please don't panic and don't be impatient; adopt a healthy lifestyle and follow some of the recommendations in the book, particularly remembering to relax, exercise and have fun, and just let nature take its course. You may be surprised and relieved to see how quickly things can happen!

Miscarriage

A miscarriage is the spontaneous loss of an embryo or foetus in the early stages of pregnancy and before the foetus has a chance of surviving outside the womb. This is generally before 24 weeks gestation, although opinion does vary here and many experts now prefer to say before 20 weeks gestation. Sadly a miscarriage is a common complication in pregnancy, and the most common reason for a gynaecological admission to hospital.

A miscarriage is a devastating blow for any couple, but when it happens after a long period of fertility problems or an IVF cycle it seems even more cruel and so very unfair. After all the waiting for that all-important positive pregnancy test, the roller coaster of emotions during the treatment cycle, not to mention the financial burden, it is particularly heart-breaking.

However I believe that understanding the causes, the risks involved and the care needed to help prevent future occurrences will be a huge step towards emotional healing. By acquiring this knowledge you will begin to feel more positive, more in control and more optimistic as you move forward to try again.

Causes of Miscarriage

There is still much we don't know about why miscarriages happen, but it is generally accepted that most are caused by chromosome abnormalities which make it impossible for the baby to develop normally. I suppose you could say it's nature's way, although that doesn't make it any easier to accept why it happened.

It is generally accepted that approximately 10–20% of all known pregnancies are thought to end in miscarriage. Some experts suggest the number may be higher, even as much as 75%. This is because it is not uncommon for someone to conceive and miscarry before they even knew they were pregnant, and then go on to have a normal period, or a period that may be just a day or so late, and they think nothing of it.

Recovery From a Miscarriage

The physical recovery: most women physically recover quite quickly after a miscarriage, with bleeding stopping in seven to ten days and their periods returning in about four to six weeks. However it is important to prevent getting an infection after miscarriage by using pads, not tampons and refraining from sex for two weeks. If the bleeding goes on for longer than ten days or if you have an offensive discharge then it is important to see your GP to make sure you have not got an infection.

The emotional recovery: the emotional healing may however take longer than the physical healing. Many women are able to shrug it off as 'nature's way', while for other women it may take a lot longer to recover from such a loss. What you have to remember is that everyone is different, and you should not beat yourself up if you feel differently about your miscarriage compared with someone else. It is normal to grieve after a miscarriage and the grief may feel as intense as with any other bereavement. Feelings of anger, despair, frustration, guilt and jealousy are common. Trying to accept what has happened instead of 'what if' will help to heal your pain in time. You will never forget your hopes and dreams, but time is a great healer and day by day things will get easier. Some women/couples find it helpful to write a letter to their baby, saying how much they love him/her and that they are so sorry they didn't get to meet him/her. Others find it helpful to have a special place in their home where they can light a candle, while others will plant a tree or a shrub.

It is important to remember that most miscarriages are a one-off occurrence and the majority of women go on to have a healthy pregnancy very soon afterwards. Less than 5% of women have two miscarriages and less than 1% have three or more.

A recurrent miscarriage is when someone has two miscarriages in a row before 20th week of pregnancy.[13] Even if you have experienced two miscarriages there is every chance that you will go on to have a healthy pregnancy. Try to remain positive and optimistic and remember that every pregnancy is different as no two eggs or sperm are ever the same.

However if you have had three miscarriages or more then it is advisable to see your GP who may refer you to a specialist to rule out any other causes. Likewise if there is a history of miscarriage in the family – if your mother experienced more than one, or if your sister did – or if you have taken a long time to conceive in between the miscarriages it is advisable to get some further tests. It is highly unlikely that there will be anything wrong, but sometimes for peace of mind, further tests are helpful. Some possibilities that need to be eliminated are:

•   Hormonal disturbances
•   Genetic problems
•   Anatomical problems in or with the womb, e.g. a septum, fibroids or polyps
•   Conditions that cause 'sticky blood' such as Hughes Syndrome, Lupus or MTHFR, a very common genetic condition that prevents the absorption of folate (folic acid) and B vitamins, resulting in increased homocysteine levels which increase blood viscosity. Thicker blood which is more prone to clotting could contribute to pregnancy loss. If you have been diagnosed with a condition of 'sticky blood' please don't panic – it is easily treated with medication.

The one thing I would say is try not to become anxious about the same thing happening again; as I said before, remember that every egg and every sperm are different, and so each embryo is unique and as a result no two pregnancies are ever the same. I think the following quote has a lot going for it:

> *Don't worry about failure – worry about the chances you miss when you don't even try.*
> Jack Canfield, *Chicken Soup for the Soul*

Secondary Infertility

Secondary infertility is defined as *the inability to become pregnant, or to carry a pregnancy to term, following the birth of one or more biological children. The birth of the first child does not involve any assisted reproductive technologies or fertility medications.*[14]

Secondary infertility is actually very common, but it is not often talked about. When a woman has conceived her first child easily, it can be quite a shock when it doesn't happen the next time as planned.

The emotional experience and grief of secondary infertility is just as distressing as primary infertility, but to others the pain is invisible because they already have a child, and the fertility problems are not always acknowledged. Often even the medical profession play it down, encouraging the couple to keep on trying.

There are just as many emotions, if not more, in women with secondary fertility problems, and those emotions are just as likely to interfere with and hijack fertility as those of women with primary fertility problems.

Some of the issues experienced by women with secondary infertility are:

- Guilt: some women wonder how they could possibly love another child as much as their first. Also, will it mean loving their first child any less? However as a mother of four children myself, I was overwhelmed by how much my 'heart' seemed to expand, spilling over with so much love for each and every child.

- Busy lifestyle: working mothers with a small child never seem to stop. There is always something to do; the list is endless – childcare, washing, cleaning and preparing meals, as well as working outside the home. They also have the added burden of worry when the child is ill and can't go to nursery or the child minder – how can they juggle work with looking after a sick child? It is no wonder working mums are often emotional wrecks! And if they are this busy how will they cope with a second child? All of these feelings circulating in their emotional brain creates even more stress!

- Worry: they may be worrying about the financial issues of having another child. Will they be able to manage with another mouth to feed and with all the expense of bringing up another child? How will they manage with another year on maternity leave? Some will worry about how they will cope with looking after a busy toddler when they are tired and worn out after sleepless nights.

- Fear: some women will experience fear about the birth itself, especially if the first birth was long and prolonged, or if they had to have a caesarean.

- Sex: or rather, lack of it! Let's face it, if you have a toddler that sneaks into your bed at night he/she will definitely put an end to any moment of passion! Also the tiredness that accompanies juggling work and childcare means that sex is not going to be high on the agenda, or a priority. So try to enlist the help of family or friends who can have your child overnight so that you can have some time together (at the right time of the cycle obviously) and a good night's sleep. Most grandparents are only too happy to oblige.

The self-help techniques in this book are equally appropriate for those of you with secondary fertility problems as they are for those trying for the first time. You may need to make a little more effort to put time aside for relaxation or meditation, or take advantage when your toddler is having an afternoon nap!

References

1. Euripides, *Iphigenia in Aulis*, c. 405 BC, as cited in Randine Lewis, PhD, *The Infertility Cure*, Little, Brown and Company, New York, 2004, p4
2. Jacky Boivin, *Fertility: The Real Story*. http://www.icsicommunity. org/_files/f/1452/Fertility%20-%20The%20Real%20Story.pdf. (accessed on 2nd June 2014)
3. Emma Innes. Five million babies have now been born by IVF - and HALF since 2007, new figures confirm. http://www.dailymail. co.uk/health/article-2462640/Five-million-babies-born-IVF-HALF-2007.html (accessed on 2nd June 2014)
4. Hfea. Fertility treatment in 2013, trends and figures. http://www. hfea.gov.uk/docs/HFEA_Fertility_Trends_and_Figures_2013.pdf (accessed 2nd June 2014)
5. Lynch C. D., Sundaram R., Maisog J. M., Sweeney A. M. and Buck Louis G. M., *Preconception stress increases the risk of infertility: results from a couple-based prospective cohort study – the LIFE study*. *Human Reproduction*, 2014, Vol. 0, No. 0 p1–9
6. Philip Quinn and Michael Pawson MB BS FRCOG, *Psychosomatic Infertility*, *European Journal of Clinical Hypnosis*, 1994, Vol. 4, p1–10
7. Alice D. Domar, *Conquering Infertility: Dr Alice Domar's Mind/Body Guide to Enhancing Fertility and Coping with Infertility*, New York, 2002
8. Robert N. Clarke, Susan C. Klock, Anne Geoghegan and David E. Travasoss, *Relationship between psychological stress and semen quality among in-vitro fertilisation patients*. *Human Reproduction*, 1999 Vol. 14 No.3 p753–758
9. Dr Elizabeth Muir, as cited in *The Mind-Body Fertility Connection* by James Schwartz, Llewellyn Publications, Minnesota, 2008, p19
10. Christopher Williams, MD, *The Fastest Way to Get Pregnant Naturally*, Hyperion, New York, 2001
11. Deepak Chopra, *Perfect Health*, Bantam Books, London, 2001
12. *Ibid*
13. Alan Beer, MD, *Is Your Body Baby Friendly?* AJR Publishing, USA, 2006
14. Resolve, The National Infertility Association. Secondary Infertility. http://www.resolve.org/about-infertility/medical-conditions/ secondary-infertility.html (accessed 2nd June 2014)

Chapter Two

Don't Let Your Emotions Hijack Your Fertility!

In this chapter I want to look at some of the emotions women experience when they are trying for a baby.

You can control your body to a certain extent – you can control what you do with it and you can control what you put into it, but can you control your mind? Are your emotions hijacking your fertility? Do you have the emotional, physical and mental space in your life for a baby?

Emotions

The word *emotion* is derived from the French word *émouvoir*. This is based on the Latin *emovere*, where *e* means 'out', and *movere* means 'to move'; i.e. to move out from the place you are in, to excite or to agitate.[1] The word *motivation* is also derived from *movere*.

Emotional wellbeing is a very important part of fertility treatment and rebalancing your emotions may contribute in a positive way as you embark on your fertility journey. But what are emotions? When someone is tearful or upset we say they are very emotional. But being emotional can mean more than just being tearful. Our emotions reflect what we're thinking and feeling. According to Bob Doyle, *Our emotions are an incredible gift that we have been given to let us know what we're thinking.*[2] It is now thought that emotion is a product of the brain and the body acting together.[3]

An emotion is a mental and bodily reaction and is associated with a variety of feelings, thoughts and behaviours. It can be triggered by a reaction to an external event, a memory of an event or by our own internal thoughts such as worry or fear. Emotions are feelings that are created by our own mental stimuli – our thinking – which then go on to influence our day-to-day life.

It is widely accepted that in Western medicine there are four main emotions, with all other emotions being derived from them. The four main emotions are Fear, Anger, Sadness and Joy.[4] In Traditional Chinese Medicine (TCM) they have expanded this and say that there are actually seven emotions, and it is thought that these emotions disturb the mind and spirit, affecting the circulation of Qi (energy) and blood, and also the balance of the internal organs. In Chinese medicine the seven emotions are Fear, Worry, Anger, Pensiveness, Sadness, Shock and Joy.[5] Chinese medicine also links these emotions with our internal organs.

In TCM:

- Fear is thought to affect the kidneys
- Worry is thought to affect the lungs and spleen
- Anger is thought to affect the liver
- Pensiveness is thought to affect the spleen
- Sadness is thought to affect the lungs and heart
- Shock is thought to affect the kidneys and heart
- Joy is thought to affect the heart

We all have feelings of anger, sadness or fear from time to time, and that is quite normal, but it is when someone is persistently angry, sad or fearful that health problems occur. It is when emotions become excessive, when they are prolonged, suppressed or go un-recognised, that they can cause disease and ill-health.

Through recent research we now know that a prolonged period of emotional stress can lead to changes within the body and can actually cause disease. Our body and mind are integrated and are part of our whole being, with one impacting on the other.

Emotional stress can interfere with our endocrine system and hormonal balance. It can impair our blood supply, circulation and blood pressure. It can interfere with our breathing and even our digestion. And yet the medical fraternity are still reluctant to admit that emotional disturbances can interfere with fertility, although recent research is showing that this is certainly the case.

The main emotions, as we discussed, are fear, worry, anger, pensiveness, sadness, shock and joy, with a whole host of other emotions being derived from them or a combination of them. Some other negative emotions that women may experience are wide-ranging and include worry, frustration, impatience, stress, anxiety, rage, jealousy, grief, despair, depression, disappointment, hostility, disbelief, guilt, lack of confidence, lack of control, lack of trust, hate, bitterness, perfectionism, ruminating and so on!

Many of the above emotions are negative emotions and so it follows that if we are experiencing negative emotions we must be thinking negative thoughts. To feel good we have to think good thoughts. When we think bad thoughts, e.g. when we complain or when we are angry, we don't feel good; instead we feel cross or irritated, and this leads to the stress response.

Quite often we think about things or wish for things that we don't want to happen, as I suspect has happened to many of you – it certainly has to me. I remember a time when we had just had our sitting room decorated and had a new carpet and new furniture – all in pale colours and tones. One evening when we were having a dinner party all I could think about was *Please don't let anyone spill anything on the carpet* etc. Guess what happened – red wine was spilt! What I should have been thinking was *our friends are going to love our new look and will take great care with the wine.*

Another time I was washing a delicate dish – one of my favourite dishes – and all the time thinking to myself *I must be careful; I don't want to break this.* It slipped out of my hands and broke into pieces! What I should have said to myself was *I really love this dish and I'm going to take great care of it.*

According to Rhonda Byrne, the Law of Attraction responds to our thoughts; however it doesn't recognise the words *don't, not* or *no.* How many times have you left for work thinking *I really don't want to be late for work today?* You then get stuck behind a tractor or a learner driver, or just get stuck in traffic – it happens all the time! Next time say *I'm going to have really good journey today and I shall be early for work.*

> People have a tendency to look at the things that they want and say 'Yes I like that, I want that.' However they also look at the things that they don't want and give them just as much energy if not more, with the idea that they can stamp it out, they can eliminate it, obliterate it. In our society we've become content with fighting against things. Fighting against cancer, fighting against poverty, fighting against drugs, fighting against terrorism, fighting against violence. We tend to fight everything we don't want, which actually creates more of a fight.
>
> Lisa Nicholls, as cited in *The Secret*, page 141[6]

In the UK 3.5 million people are fighting to overcome infertility. And it is the same thought processes that go on:

- *I don't want my period to come* (contrast with *I want to miss my period* or *I know I will be pregnant*)
- *I don't want another miscarriage* (c/w *I'm going to have a healthy pregnancy*)

- *I don't want mid-cycle spotting (c/w My cycle will be normal this month)*
- *I don't want the endometriosis to return (c/w I'm pleased the surgery was successful)*
- *I don't want this IVF to fail (c/w I believe this IVF will work)*

We have to change the way we think! By changing the way we think, we change the way we feel and behave. Every negative thought is a stressful thought and that makes us feel stressed, angry or sad etc. That in turn evokes the stress response which plays havoc with the hypothalamus and our hormones, interfering with our fertility – we shall learn more about that later in the book.

> *When we direct our thoughts properly we can control our emotions.*
>
> W. Clement Stone (1902–2002)

> *Your emotions and your body are inseparable.*
> Howard R. and Martha E. Lewis, *Psychosomatics*

The positive emotions are derived from joy and include love, happiness, excitement, relief, contentment, belief and trust. When we are happy and content we release our 'feel-good' hormones, which make us feel relaxed and activate the relaxation response, which is the opposite of the fight-or-flight response. This is how we should be feeling most of the time! We can't feel happy and sad at the same time! More about this later in the book. I shall show you how to relax and activate the relaxation response, reducing stress and turning on those positive feelings.

However when we worry or are afraid or lack confidence, these are negative emotions and lead to the stress response. Fear, anger and sadness are the principle negative emotions, with other feelings or emotions being derived from them. Worry, pensiveness and shock are related to the anxiety that stems from fear.

Fear

Fear is an emotion that is present in us and is a part of what helped us evolve. Fear can be brought about by a perceived threat and is a basic survival mechanism and part of the fight-or-flight response. Fear is one of the emotions that was very important to primitive man to ensure his survival; and even though we do not usually have to face the same life-or-death threats as our ancestors, the fear response has remained even though it may not be as appropriate to our modern world.[7]

As humans we experience two different types of fear, but it's important to realise that our physiological fear – the fear that protects us – is very different from our psychological fear. Psychological fear is when there is no danger to our life, but it is a fear that we create in our own minds with our thoughts. I believe it is psychological fear that my patients face.

The biggest fear that my patients face is that this period of infertility is never going to end. They fear that they may never have a baby. Women begin to feel hopeless and powerless and feel as though they've been given a life sentence. But in actual fact it isn't, and in the ensuing chapters you will find out how to overcome this fear of never becoming a mum, because it is just a fear and you will overcome it and you will have a child one day, one way or another – you must believe that.

Fear leads to worry – women worry that they may never conceive naturally. They worry that they will have to resort to IVF. Women also worry when they are going through IVF:

- They're afraid that their period won't arrive in time for the baseline scan
- They're afraid that their ovaries won't respond to the drugs
- They're afraid that that there won't be any or enough eggs
- They're afraid that the egg collection may be painful
- They're afraid that their partner won't be able to provide a sperm sample on the day
- They're afraid that once collected, the eggs won't fertilise
- They're afraid that the embryos won't survive until day three or even day five for blastocyst transfer
- And finally, they're afraid that the IVF won't be successful and that they will have a negative pregnancy test

One of my patients was so fearful of the IVF not working. In other words, she was scared of how she would react and of what would lie ahead if this IVF – her third – was not successful.

Obviously all this worry is not doing anyone any good at all. The fear and worry is evoking the stress response, i.e. the fight-or-flight response, and that is something we need to avoid as I shall explain a bit later on. There is absolutely no need to be afraid of IVF or its different stages. Later on in the book I will show you how to overcome this fear and embrace IVF for the scientific miracle and wonder that it really is.

Being positive throughout the cycle and really *feeling* positive will help. Focus on the positive things that you can do and can control, such as eating plenty of fruit and vegetables, drinking plenty of water and having enough sleep, all of which will improve the environment that the eggs are growing in. Be grateful for the chance to have IVF in the first place, and thankful to all the medical staff for their help and expertise. Trust them – they're the experts! They have seen hundreds of people like you and treated them successfully! Another tip is to be mindful – enjoy and experience every moment of your life, and don't let negative thoughts get the better of you. There is so much more on coping and how to change your emotions and way of thinking later on in the book.

Worry

Worry is an emotion that is derived from fear. Worry is a misuse of our imagination to generate negative fantasies. Worry is thinking negative thoughts about an anticipated disaster or threat or other issues. Worry is when our brain creates a stressful situation. Our brains are so highly developed that just thinking about a negative outcome will result in our bodies responding in a stressful way. Worry is like sitting in a rocking chair – you can worry all day but it gets you nowhere fast! Worry is worthless and only brings with it negative results. Worry is just negative self-talk that distracts the mind from focusing on a positive outcome.

Most of the things we worry about will never happen anyway. We worry about all sorts of things and regardless of what we are worrying about it will still evoke the stress response. Some of my patients worry that this period of infertility is never going to end. Others worry that they will never become a mother or that they will have to resort to IVF, and then they worry that the IVF won't work.

Changing the way we think will stop us worrying! Challenge those thoughts and beliefs and if you notice yourself worrying then say 'STOP.' Instead of worrying, think about all the positive things you are doing to help your fertility, and try to put the things that are out of your control out of your mind. I'm always telling my patients not to try and control the uncontrollable!

Notice when you are worrying about something that you can't possibly control, and accept that you can't control things like the number of follicles growing, or how many eggs are fertilised, and instead think about the aspects of your fertility that you can control, such as making sure you are having plenty of sleep, eating healthily and setting aside some time for relaxation or exercise. Focusing on the positive things you are doing, the things that you *can* control, will help you feel so much better about your treatment.

Anxiety

This is another emotion that is derived from worry and fear. Anxiety is when someone worries constantly although there is no real threat, and to a point where they can't function properly. A panic attack is the most severe form of anxiety.

Anxiety is a state of inner turmoil and is a natural response to a threat, but it can also be an overreaction to a situation. Anxiety can be good for us in small doses because it can sharpen our attention and help us focus. An example of this is performance anxiety if we have to give a presentation at work etc. Actors actually welcome some performance anxiety as it keeps them focused and on edge, and as a result they deliver a better performance.

Social anxiety is similar to performance anxiety, but occurs when people are consumed by a fear of meeting and talking to other people, or even being seen in public. One of my patients had had such a hard time with bullying in work that although she had left her place of employment, she was so anxious about bumping into her ex-colleagues in the local supermarket that she would not go there. Even though this anxiety was nothing to do with her fertility, it still evoked the stress response, having a negative impact on her emotions and her hormones and interfering with her fertility.

Many women become anxious in the second half of their cycle because they are worried that they haven't conceived again and that another month will go by and they are not pregnant. When they do conceive then for some women their anxiety rockets because they're afraid of having a miscarriage. Women who have had IVF will often become very anxious in the second week of the two-week wait as they're afraid the IVF won't work.

I shall show you later on in the book how to change your thoughts and how to overcome these feelings of anxiety.

Anger

Holding onto anger is like grasping a hot coal with the intention of throwing it at someone else; you are the one getting burned.
Gautama Buddha (563–483 BC), founder of Buddhism

Everyone gets angry at some time in their life, and it is a strong, uncomfortable emotional response which we must learn to control. When anger gets out of control it can lead to physical and mental health risks. Anger happens when we feel we have been wronged in some way, for example in road rage, or when we have feelings of hostility towards another person.

Anger can manifest itself for so many reasons in women trying to conceive. Women will often feel very angry (as well as upset) when a close friend, colleague or family member becomes pregnant, particularly if that person conceived easily. One of my patients was so angry with her husband because his low sperm count meant that they had to have IVF treatment. She found this very difficult to come to terms with because she just wanted to get pregnant naturally.

Are you feeling angry about something or towards someone? Think about why you are feeling angry and what is causing this feeling. Can you change it? Can you stop feeling angry?

Jealousy

This emotion is linked to anger. Stop feeling jealous – it's not a good feeling and all it does is eat you up inside. Jealousy is a strong negative emotion that evokes the stress response and may consist of feelings of anger, resentment, inadequacy, helplessness, disgust, insecurity and bitterness that some women experience when they hear that a friend or someone close to them becomes pregnant, or if they see a pregnant woman in a shop. If a teenage girl gets pregnant accidentally or a woman who, in their opinion, doesn't deserve to get pregnant because of drug or alcohol dependency, becomes pregnant the resulting feelings of jealousy and rage can drive some women crazy – it seems as though the whole world is against them.

There will always be pregnant women around you, either in work or a close friend or a family member, and of course it can be difficult not to feel jealous when everyone around you seems to be getting pregnant. Of course you will be affected by it because you're a sensitive person and this is something close to your own heart. Of course you are going to be upset, that's only natural. But don't let it get to you and don't fall victim to it or let it affect you for too long.

If we think about the Law of Attraction, when we really want or wish for something it is attracted to us. Think about this – have you ever decided to buy a new car or change your car? You choose the make of car you like and then suddenly out of nowhere that particular make of car seems to pop up everywhere! You park next to one, or one passes you on the motorway, or there is one in your street. The law of attraction is attracting that car to you.

Now think about the law of attraction working for you when you see a pregnant woman, and instead of feeling jealous or angry, feel instead the glow, warmth and joy inside you as you realise you are attracting your dream to you. Imagine that every time you see or hear of someone being pregnant, pregnancy is coming closer to you. You are attracting being pregnant yourself! This is a much more positive way of dealing with it and instead of the negative feelings eating you up inside, which only push your dream further away, your positive feelings will work with you to achieve your dream.

Women may also experience jealousy if someone they know has the money to pay for IVF while they are having to wait for the NHS, and they feel that life is so unfair. There are many things in life that you can't change and instead of getting upset over them, take back control and choose to remain calm, and try to do the breathing exercises that are described later in the book. There are ways however to overcome these feelings and I shall show you how to cope positively with them later in the book.

Disbelief

This is linked to anger, and is a feeling you experience when you do not or cannot believe that something is true or real. For example when a pregnancy test is negative, or when someone has been told they have premature ovarian failure and are in an early menopause, or even when a close friend tells you she is pregnant. Disbelief is linked to feelings of anger and sadness.

Hostility

Hostility can be seen as an emotionally charged angry behaviour. Women may experience hostility towards other women who are pregnant, or even to their partner if they have a problem with their sperm. Some woman will be hostile towards their partner if they feel he is not taking the fertility problems seriously and doing something about it, such as cutting down on alcohol, stopping smoking, or improving an unhealthy diet. These feelings can then build and lead to resentment.

Resentment

Another negative emotion similar to anger or hatred, this is a feeling that you may get when you have been the subject of unfair treatment. It is quite common in women who are trying everything there is in order to become pregnant, only to find that other women who they believe have no right to get pregnant get pregnant accidentally, or that women who smoke and drink to excess get pregnant easily. It seems to them that life is unfair and everything is stacked against them.

Grief and Sadness

*I had two bereavements this year. IVF is worse than bereavement
– it's the hardest thing I've ever gone through. I feel as though
I've just woken from a bad dream.*

Grief is a natural, healthy and normal response to a significant emotional loss – the emotional suffering experienced after the devastation of a miscarriage or stillbirth, or even a negative pregnancy test. Crying is normal and a natural part of grieving. It is important to grieve healthily and to acknowledge sad feelings when they arise, accepting that they are caused by the loss and by memories of that loss going through your mind.[8]

If you have experienced such a loss, life appears so unfair and so cruel. Allow yourself a reasonable time to grieve but after that try to avoid dwelling on it and don't allow your thoughts to focus on the 'what if's. Don't dig deeper to try to find a reason as you will only make yourself more upset. Don't underestimate your loss, but acknowledge that you are grieving and that it is part of a normal process. You may never forget your loss but what you have to accept is that this time will pass and you will heal.

Everyone will deal with their grief in different ways. Some people find it easier to write things down or to write a letter to their baby. In the letter you can say how sad you are that he or she didn't make it, how much you love him/her and how much you are going to miss him/her. Some people like to honour their baby's memory by planting a tree or a shrub or by having a private ceremony and lighting a candle or reading a poem or a prayer. This can help you and your partner achieve a sense of closure to your mourning and may help you to let go and move on.

It is important that you recognise normal grieving as opposed to clinical depression, because grieving can sometimes trigger depression. This happens when the grieving process goes disastrously wrong, when women misuse or allow their imaginations to get carried away with them and project the sense of loss into the future.

It is important to grieve healthily and to recognise the sad feelings when they arise, and then let them go without adding to them or building them up in your imagination. Some women find the best way to grieve over their loss is to set aside a particular time of day when they can think about their baby. By setting this special time aside you might find that for the rest of the day you are able to concentrate on your job or the housework or other activities such as exercise or meeting friends for a coffee, without always focusing on your grief.

Prolonged sadness can lead to depression, which may feel like a deep emotional numbness.

Depression

This can be caused by a number of things including prolonged grief, guilt, anxiety, stress, feelings of hopelessness or worthlessness or recurrent thoughts of imagining a childless future.

Depression is rising quickly in our 21st century society and it is the way our lives have changed and how we live them that results in so many people being unable to cope with the pressures of everyday life. It is important that if you think you may be depressed then you must see your GP as depression can negatively affect the chances of getting pregnant.

Pioneering work by Dr Alice Domar showed that women who were struggling to conceive were more depressed than fertile women. She also discovered that the longer they had been trying to get pregnant, the more depressed these women were. The most depressed women had been trying to conceive for two to three years.

Another discovery that Dr Domar made was that infertility patients were as depressed and anxious as patients suffering with life-threatening conditions such as cancer.[9] However her further research showed that when these women with infertility participated in a mind/body programme they became significantly less depressed, and it also made it easier for them to conceive.[10]

Pensiveness

Pensiveness can mean overthinking, and includes guilt and ruminating about the past.

> *How you see your future is more important than what happened in the past.*
>
> Zig Ziglar

We often feel guilty when we dwell on things that have happened in the past, and how we wished we could have changed things or reacted in a different way. Things that have happened cannot be changed and therefore there is no point at all in brooding over them. Women may feel guilty because they may have had a termination in the past and feel that they are now being punished for it. The fact is, these feelings may have only come to light now that they are struggling with fertility. They are grieving for the baby they are trying to conceive as well as the one they lost.

Do not waste one moment in regret, because to think feelingly of the mistakes of the past is to re-infect yourself.
Neville Goddard (1905–1972) *New Thought* author

Ruminating

Ruminating is a negative emotion that focuses on bad experiences that happened in the past. It is associated with anxiety. When people ruminate they overthink and become obsessed with retracing past mistakes or other negative events in the past. This happens sometimes with women who have experienced one or more miscarriages or a failed IVF cycle.

It is important to get off the treadmill and start focusing on positive things. Women often think *I wish I hadn't had that cup of coffee/glass of wine, or gone to the gym, or gone back to work too soon.* In actual fact these things probably won't have made any difference at all to the outcome, so please stop worrying about it. You're only making things worse for yourself.

Shock

Shock is classed as one of the seven emotions in Chinese medicine. Mental shock scatters the *Qi* according to TCM. In Western medicine it is thought of as severe agitation and classed as severe anxiety, and is linked with fright and fear. An example could be when a woman is told she is in premature ovarian

51

failure and will not be able to conceive naturally, or possibly during an early pregnancy scan if there is no heartbeat detected. Such things can be seen to be so cruel and so unexpected that it could create a shock to the system. Thankfully these experiences are very rare.

Complaining

Complaining is not an emotion as such, but it is a negative frame of mind.

> Gratitude is riches, complaint is poverty.
>
> Doris Day

> The more you complain about your problems, the more problems you will have to complain about.
>
> Zig Ziglar

Complaining is a negative experience and it is so easy to get caught up in it, especially when someone says the weather is awful, or at work when someone complains about the hours or the workload or the lack of a pay rise. When you complain you only see things from a negative perspective and it appears that we are a complaining nation!

People complain about so many things: a poor meal, poor service, the long queue in a shop, the traffic – the list is endless. One of the biggest things people complain about is our health service. When there is a real crisis the NHS can be fantastic, but people are always complaining about it. In my opinion the people who complain bitterly about the NHS are the ones that probably don't really need urgent treatment anyway!

People feel that complaining about something will make them feel better or ease the situation, but in actual fact it leaves you feeling much worse. Next time it rains think about how lucky we are to have enough water to live, and be thankful for our beautiful green countryside, because without all our rain we wouldn't be able to have fresh water to drink or wash, or to do our laundry.

We often hear a lot of complaints but we rarely hear people saying 'thank you' for good service or a great meal. People will write a letter or send an email complaining about something, but how often do we write and say 'thank you' for excellent service? So next time you think about complaining, stop yourself and think about something positive instead – you will be amazed by how much better it will make you feel. If you hear someone else complain try to turn their complaint around into a positive statement – they may laugh and be surprised, but you will have done them a favour because they too will feel better for your positive frame of mind.

When I was doing my hypnotherapy training, one of the exercises we had to do was to ask the student sitting next to us 'What has been good about your day/week?' We then had to draw out of them as many positive statements as we could, saying 'And what else was good? What else?' until they had listed at least ten good things that had happened to them that day or that week. It seemed an unusual exercise, but now it is obvious that we were encouraging people to focus on the positive aspects of their lives, and to remember the good things that happened instead of focusing on the negative aspects.

So when you or your partner start to complain, saying 'I've had a terrible day at work', STOP! And instead think about what was GOOD about your day! Instead of complaining about how long you had to wait to be seen in the hospital for a blood test or a scan, think about how pleased you were to actually get an appointment, how helpful the medical staff were and how they were still able to give you a smile even though they were frantically busy. Think how lucky we are to have such a fantastic healthcare system that is free!

Joy

When everything is going well in our lives we feel happy, relaxed and content. We should be feeling like this most of the time. There are occasions when we experience a feeling of great exhilaration and happiness, and everyone will have felt this happy emotion at some time or other – a period in your life that you don't want to come to an end; possibly a wonderful holiday, your wedding day or seeing that positive blue line on a pregnancy test. It is a wonderful feeling to feel happy, but sometimes overexcitement can wreak just as much havoc with our biology and physiology as negative feelings. Sometimes we cry tears of joy because we are so happy!

There is a fine line between stress and overexcitement – both produce vast amounts of adrenaline and cortisol. The secret is to be able to distinguish between them and recognise the feelings for what they are.

Obviously it is much better to be excited than stressed, and it is impossible to feel stressed and relaxed at the same time as one biological process will override the other. Someone who lives a hectic life of working and playing hard could be considered, in Traditional Chinese Medicine, to have excessive excitement which is also thought to be a form of continual mental stimulation, which is a more negative aspect of joy.[11] Perfectionism could be linked to this.

Perfectionism

Sometimes… when you hold out for everything, you walk away with nothing.

Ally McBeal

54

Are you a perfectionist?

Perfectionism in psychology is a personality trait characterized by a person's striving for flawlessness and setting excessively high performance standards, accompanied by overly critical self-evaluations and concerns regarding others' evaluations.[12]

So many of my patients have the perfect lifestyle: both partners have their dream jobs, they have the perfect house and they have been able to achieve everything they have wanted in their life – except having a baby.

So many women have achieved everything they dreamed of: they have passed every exam and they have been offered every job they applied for, but these things have been within their control to a certain extent. They studied hard for exams and studied hard to get the perfect job, but now they want to start a family they can't control their fertility.

That is the most frustrating thing for these women; they can't accept that they can't control their own bodies. They are doing everything in their power to become pregnant – they have read all the books and scoured the internet for information. They have made lifestyle changes by giving up alcohol and coffee, they are taking their multivitamins and omega 3, they are charting their cycles meticulously on their smartphones and timing their intercourse to perfection, but still they can't get pregnant.

But all this constant thinking and trying to control this process of getting pregnant is actually creating stress within the body as they strive to get the perfect outcome. Internal stress and frustration, as well as the feelings of inadequacy and impatience as they realise they are failing in their ability to achieve what they think they want most in their life – a baby.

High achievers are so used to putting themselves under pressure that they don't notice the tension they are creating within their body, because to them it feels normal. However it is not normal and instead the body is under constant stress, which means that the sympathetic nervous system – or the fight-or-flight response – is continually switched on. This means that the hypothalamus, which controls our hormones and fertility, can't function properly and so the ratio of hormones needed to support fertility is unbalanced and the body fails to conceive. Sadly most of these women can't see this; they are in denial but they are the ones who get angry when someone says 'Relax and it will happen.'

If this sounds like you, then try to lighten up a bit. Practise the relaxation and meditation tips later in the book and allow yourself a bit of 'me' time instead of cleaning the house spotlessly, or answering your emails on the dot. Make time for yourself – the housework and the emails will be there tomorrow! Let the ironing build up and go and do some fun activities with your partner instead – take a day off and go somewhere nice for lunch, or go for a walk and take a luxury picnic. Not only will you feel better for it, but it will also strengthen your relationship as you take some time to enjoy each other's company.

References

1. Oxford Dictionary. Emotion. http://www.oxforddictionaries. com/definition/english/emotion (accessed on 14th June 2014)
2. Bob Doyle as quoted in Rhonda Byrne, *The Secret*, Simon and Schuster UK Ltd, 2006, p30
3. John Ratey, *A User's Guide to the Brain*, Little, Brown and Company, London, 2001
4. John Ratey, *A User's Guide to the Brain*, Little, Brown and Company, London, 2001
5. Giovanni Maciocia, *Diagnosis in Chinese Medicine*, Churchill Livingstone, London, 2004
6. Lisa Nicholls, as cited in Rhonda Byrne, *The Secret*, Simon and Schuster UK Ltd, 2006, p141
7. John Ratey, *A User's Guide to the Brain*, Little, Brown and Company, London, 2001
8. Joe Griffin and Ivan Tyrrell, *How to Lift Depression Fast*, HG Publishing, Great Britain, 2004
9. Alice D. Domar, *Conquering Infertility: Dr Alice Domar's Mind/Body Guide to Enhancing Fertility and Coping with Infertility*, New York, 2002
10. Alice D. Domar, *Conquering Infertility: Dr Alice Domar's Mind/Body Guide to Enhancing Fertility and Coping with Infertility,* New York, 2002
11. Giovanni Maciocia, *Diagnosis in Chinese Medicine*, Churchill Livingston, London, 2004
12. Wikipedia. Perfectionism. https://en.wikipedia.org/wiki/ Perfectionism_(psychology) (accessed on 14th June 2014)

Chapter Three

The Origin of Emotions

How the Brain Works

In this chapter I want to explain a little bit about how the brain works and where emotions originate. Understanding that there is an emotional part of the brain will make it easier for you to understand and control these emotions.

Human beings have an average of 50,000 thoughts a day. Our minds are often full of negative thoughts and emotions which can sometimes get out of control and ruin our lives and impact on our fertility. These thoughts often play over and over in our minds, becoming tangled up, filling our minds with rubbish and negative beliefs that are simply not true. These negative beliefs create internal or psychological stress, leading to:

- Worrying about things that may never happen or are out of our control
- Dwelling on negative outcomes
- Criticising or blaming ourselves
- Imagining the worst-case scenario
- Holding ourselves to unrealistic standards
- Feeling guilty
- Grief
- Unrelenting doubts and fears

By understanding how the brain works we can untangle this mess and remove all the rubbish from our minds, allowing for clearer thought processes and a healthier outlook on life.

Our brain is made up of two parts – the conscious and the subconscious. The conscious part of the brain is the brain as we know it, and the part that interacts with the world. It is linked to a vast intellectual resource which is our intellectual mind. It is the intellectual mind that allows us to read and write, use a computer, mobile phone etc. This is how we differ from other animals because they don't possess the same intellectual resource. When we are using our intellectual mind we generally cope well with life. It is a positive mind and allows us to think rationally. It will also allow us to make a proper assessment of any given situation.

There is however another part of our brain and this is our subconscious. This is what we think of as the original part of the brain, and the primitive part as it has been derived from the time when we were primitive hunter-gatherers. This is also what we think of as the emotional part of the brain. The most important part of this is the amygdala, also known as the fight-or-flight centre. It works closely with two other primitive areas – the hippocampus which holds all our primitive and sometimes inappropriate behavioural actions such as obsessive compulsive disorder (OCD) for example compulsive eating, and the hypothalamus which helps us regulate chemical responses, or controls our hormones in the body and brain.

So let's imagine what would happen if, say, we were attacked (hypothetically) by a polar bear. What would happen? Our anxiety would go up, our heart would race, our stomach would churn and we would be off like a shot! We would lose intellectual control and move from the intellectual part of the brain into the primitive brain – our fight-or-flight and survival centre.

This reaction would be perfectly normal because it is designed to save our life. However there is a slight problem here, because as advanced as our brain is it can't distinguish between a real threat and a perceived threat. This means that when we become anxious or stressed the same thing happens, but it may be a more gradual process. We lose intellectual control – have you noticed how difficult it is to make a decision when you are really stressed? This is because the primitive (subconscious) brain takes over. This primitive brain always works within the parameters of anxiety, stress, anger or depression. Have you noticed how stupid someone appears when they have road rage? They are completely irrational!

If our subconscious mind thinks that our life is in danger it will step in to help. The primitive mind is a negative mind and always sees things from the worst possible perspective – the glass is always half empty. It has to think this way for our preservation – it doesn't think *Ah, that polar bear has already eaten*, does it? It immediately assumes the polar bear will attack us!

What is it then that causes us to move from the intellectual or conscious part of the brain to the primitive, emotional or subconscious part? Well, it is anxiety. Anxiety is brought about by negative thinking – it is not the things that happen to us in life that cause us stress, but the way we think, deal with and react to those things. It's our perception of those things. Every negative thought is converted into anxiety. We can create anxiety by negatively forecasting the future – we will never be able to afford that; I'll never become pregnant; we'll never be able to afford IVF; I'll never have a baby; I'll never be a mum; what if I have another miscarriage etc.

The mind can't tell the difference between imagination and reality, and every negative thought we have is accumulated and stored. We say it is stored in a stress bucket. Thankfully we have a way of emptying our stress bucket and it is known as REM (rapid eye movement) sleep. At night, during REM sleep, the brain goes over the events of the day and changes them from emotional memories to narrative memories. A narrative memory is one we have control over. We do this by moving them from the primitive brain to the intellectual brain while we sleep.

Most people are familiar with how REM works – if something happens to upset you, when, say, your period comes, you may be really upset. You tell your husband or partner and he says 'Don't be upset, we can always try again next month.' But you still feel upset and can't stop worrying about it, and you're still thinking about it when you go to bed. During REM sleep you re-run the event and metaphorically (dreaming) move it from the primitive or emotional mind to the intellectual mind, and so when you wake in the morning you will still be thinking about it but it doesn't seem so bad and you will probably think *Oh well, we can try again next month and it gives me more time to relax/improve my diet.*

Some people can wake each morning with their stress bucket emptied and can start the day without worry or stress. Others can't and instead wake up anxious about the day ahead; why is this? Well, some people pile so much into their stress bucket that it will overflow. For one reason or another REM is restricted to about 20% of our sleep pattern and can only empty 20% of our bucket. So if we overdo things, then the mind will wake us up at night. We know when it is the mind waking us up and not something outside because we wake up wide awake and often feel quite sad. Often we can't get back to sleep again because our mind is going round and round because we are actively overthinking. Now we are in a vicious circle. The more we have in our stress bucket, the more time spent in our primitive brain, and the more we are encouraged to be negative and that stresses us out even more, and so it goes on.

So, we need to break the circle by restricting the amount we pile into the bucket. We need to change the way we think and start concentrating on the positive things in life. We know when this happens because we start to sleep better and wake feeling more positive and refreshed in the morning.

Our primitive brain has not evolved since we were hunter-gatherers. When the caveman looked out of the cave and saw snow, ice or danger and he couldn't go out to hunt, he would pull the skins over his head and wouldn't interact until the situation had changed. We can see the similarity to this in modern-day symptoms of depression when we retreat and stop going out and socialising with our friends; when we avoid answering the phone and so on. Many of my patients stop socialising because they are watching what they eat and drink, and often stop seeing many of their friends, particularly if those friends have got a baby. It is easy to see how they can become withdrawn from society, and this can lead to sadness and depression.

But when early man did go out to hunt he got rewards for carrying out these evolutionary processes. They got a reward when they hunted and gathered, and successfully supported themselves and their families. Human beings are better as a tribe than as individuals, and so they got a reward when they interacted with others. The reward they got they definitely recognised because it helped them feel better about life. They felt motivated, but most of all it was a coping mechanism; it helped them cope with day-to-day activities, it helped them cope better with physical fear, it made them braver and it even helped them cope with pain. No doubt they were pleased. And now we know what that reward is – it's a chemical response in the brain that produces various neurotransmitters that act as catalysts for that sort of healthy mental behaviour. And the neurotransmitter that we talk about most because it is the most important is serotonin. When we produce a constant flow of serotonin we are happy and contented people coping well with life. So how do we make sure we have a constant flow of serotonin? Well, we need to operate within the positive parameters like early man, and although we do not have to go out to hunt, we do have to interact in a positive way, be active in a positive way and think in a positive way. Because when we do we produce patterns in the brain that give us that constant flow of serotonin and that makes us feel good. Thinking positively will also have a positive effect on our physiology and our health.

When we start to think negatively, and a negative thought is always a bad thought, then we become anxious, and when we are anxious we produce an overload of adrenaline and cortisol – the stress hormones. A constant supply of these stress hormones (great for running away from polar bears) creates psychological stress in the body and this leads to physical illness and health problems.[1]

Effects of Psychological Stress

Now that we understand how the brain works we can look at the effects of stress on the body. We don't necessarily need to feel stressed out because the effects of psychological stress may be the result of our emotions such as fear, despair, jealousy or anger, or it can be the result of actual stress when life's demands exceed our ability to meet those demands – in other words, when we are piling too much into our stress bucket.[2] It's not what happens to us in life that causes stress, but the way we react, deal with and respond to those events that makes a difference.

> *There is little difference in people, but that little difference makes a big difference. The little difference is attitude. The big difference is whether it is positive or negative.*
>
> W. Clement Stone

So let's talk about actual stress for a moment as we've discussed our emotions earlier in the book. Everyone will experience and deal with stress in different ways. Stress happens when your mind believes it is in some form of danger – it could be physical or emotional. It occurs when your mind believes that it can't cope with a certain situation and you feel frustrated, anxious or angry. In small doses stress can be good for us because it helps us stay focused and alert. It can help us gain confidence and helps us with creativity and learning. It gives us a buzz before a presentation or sports challenge and helps us stay focused at an interview. And of course, it helps us with survival by responding quickly when we face an emergency. It is only when stress becomes overwhelming that it causes problems to our health, our relationships, our work and our way of life.

Stress seems to be the new addiction, and suddenly it is fashionable to be busy, busy, busy. Being busy soon becomes a way of life and being stressed out starts to feel normal. Some people appear to thrive on stress. However we may not realise how much it is actually affecting us, and the effect it has on our bodies and our health. Don't allow stress to hijack your life.

Some of the commonest causes of stress include work or career issues, worries about money, relationship issues, uncertainty about the future, family problems, lack of control, low self-esteem and social issues. Trying to get pregnant is stressful enough in itself but if there are other issues involved things can spiral out of control and it soon becomes apparent how chronic stress affects our health and happiness.

High levels of stress mean we can't think clearly and have difficulty making decisions. We end up making mistakes or saying or doing things that we regret, e.g. in family feuds or road rage.

Stress can manifest itself in so many different ways:

- Feeling run down or catching colds and flu frequently
- Menstrual irregularity – periods may become infrequent, more painful or clotty, or may stop altogether, (remember a normal cycle is essential for conception)

- Frequent headaches or migraines
- Feeling tearful much of the time or bursting into tears easily
- Irritable bowel syndrome (IBS)
- Stomach upsets and digestive problems such as acid reflux
- Shortness of breath
- Frequent sighing or yawning
- Poor sleeping patterns – either sleepless nights or sleeping too much
- General muscular aches and pains
- Palpitations, heart fluttering or chest pain
- Feeling irritated by relatively small issues
- Feeling bad-tempered and argumentative
- Inability to think straight or make decisions
- Inability to cope with noise

As human beings are 'higher animals' we have to face lots of different types of stress including physical, physiological, psychological (internal stress – thinking/worrying) and social stress. Recent research shows that psychological stress is a primary cause of inflammatory diseases.

The Stress Response

So let's have a look at what actually happens to our bodies when we are stressed. The stress response is when the brain uses both the nervous system and the endocrine system (our hormones) to respond to a threat. This may be a real threat; a physical threat, for example if we have to swerve when someone cuts across in front of us when driving, or it could be a perceived threat, which is a threat that we are imagining.

When the brain thinks that we are in some kind of danger the hypothalamus releases a hormone called corticotrophin releasing hormone (CRH). This stimulates the pituitary to produce another hormone called adrenocorticotrophic hormone

(ACTH) which then stimulates the adrenal glands that sit on top of the kidneys to produce cortisol. Cortisol, as we know it, is the main stress hormone.[3] This sequence of events is known as the hypothalamus/pituitary/adrenal axis, or HPA axis.

Cortisol is an essential hormone which is needed to maintain important physiological processes when under pressure. It plays a major role in the body's metabolism and in controlling our mood. It also plays a part in maintaining balance in our immune system, digestive system and blood pressure. Cortisol is essential to our survival and flight-or-fight response. However problems arise when there is too much cortisol in the body, or when it is present continuously. These chronically raised levels of cortisol contribute to so many of our health problems including obesity, high blood pressure, diabetes, Alzheimer's disease, depression, fertility problems and so on.[4]

In their book *The Healing Code*, Alexander Loyd and Ben Johnson compare the body to a battleship. When everything is calm the ship will chug along quietly through the water. Some of the sailors will be sailing the ship, others will be involved in maintenance and repair work, others will be cleaning and scrubbing the decks, and others will be resting or eating. However as soon as the ship comes under attack, all hands are on deck! Repair and maintenance is not important, nor is cleaning, eating or resting. Everyone is involved in the 'survival' of the ship.

It is exactly the same in the human body. When we are stressed, our brain believes we are under attack, like the ship. Everything that is not essential to our survival in the next few minutes gets put on hold. The heart beats faster to pump blood into the arms or legs to 'fight or flight', while the digestive and immune and reproductive systems are put on hold – what's the point of digesting that last meal, warding off a cough or becoming pregnant if you are not going to survive the next few minutes? And besides, all the body's excess energy is needed for survival. This was all very well in our caveman days, but what about 21ˢᵗ century living? The big problem is that our brain hasn't evolved or changed in the way it responds to stress, and the stresses of today are very different to those experienced by our ancestors.

The problem we have today is that juggling our busy lives means that we live in an almost continual state of fight or flight. And so, although these changes are designed to save our life, continual stress with its raised levels of cortisol is actually very damaging to our health. That excess cortisol racing around the body is harming us, causing damage to our organs and impairing our immune system. Unlike our ancestors we cannot run away from our stresses. The very action of fighting or fleeing from danger used up the excess cortisol and adrenaline, but we cannot escape from pressures at work, traffic jams, our mobile phones, emails and bank statements. And so we end up living with abnormally high levels of cortisol in our bodies constantly, which is much longer than the few minutes our bodies were evolved to cope with. It stands to reason then that if our bodies are in a constant state of anxiety the immune, digestive and reproductive systems must be put on hold for much of the time.

Constant stress results in a depleted immune system, a digestive system that's out of sorts, a reproductive system that's on hold, higher levels of cholesterol and increased blood pressure. Blood is thicker and more viscous because if we were in danger of bleeding to death following a fight, it would clot more quickly to stop the bleeding. This does not help when we are constantly under stress as it can lead to heart attack and stroke, or in the case of fertility may even prevent implantation. [5]

References

1. Adapted from *How the Brain Works* by kind permission from David Newton, the Clifton Practice, Bristol, http://www.cpht.co.uk
2. Shawn Talbot, *The Cortisol Connection*, Hunter House, Alameda,2007
3. *Ibid*
4. *Ibid*
5. Shawn Talbot, *The Cortisol Connection*, Hunter House, Alameda,2007; Alexander Loyd and Ben Johnson, *The Healing Code*, Hodder and Stoughton, London, 2011

Chapter Four

Stress-related Diseases

In Chapter Three we saw how constant stress affects our hormonal and reproductive system, and how it can also result in a depleted immune system, a digestive system that's out of sorts, higher levels of cholesterol and increased blood pressure. It's not surprising then that so many health issues are caused by stress.

Let's have a look at the many diseases that are related to stress. Stress-related diseases happen when our brain over-responds to the stresses of day-to-day life and reacts by producing a continual flow of cortisol in response to those stresses.

Cortisol in small doses is vital to our survival, but in excessive amounts it increases our risk of a variety of illnesses and diseases. Research has shown that chronically high levels of cortisol can have a detrimental effect on the body in many ways, and in particular in the areas that can directly or indirectly affect fertility:

- The reproductive system
- The cardiovascular system
- The immune system
- The digestive system
- By causing depression
- By accelerating the ageing process

Stress and the Reproductive System

The medical fraternity have recognised for some time that stress can cause various health problems such as high blood pressure, cardiovascular disease, irritable bowel syndrome, skin complaints and so on. However when it comes to reproduction there is still this myth that stress does not affect fertility. In fact they go as far as to say that infertility is not caused by stress, but infertility itself can cause stress! An eminent professor only recently said that *The evidence for stress causing infertility simply isn't there*[1], although he does agree that infertility causes severe depression and great anxiety. There is more and more evidence emerging all the time to suggest that stress *does* interfere with fertility and conception.

★

Patient 8

This patient was 36 years old and had been trying to conceive for the past two years. She had had an IUI in the previous three months which sadly resulted in a miscarriage. She was keen to try acupuncture and other relaxation techniques to reduce her stress levels before going for another IUI in a couple of months' time.

When I first met this patient the only way I can describe her is 'fizzing'! She was all over the place – she was constantly fidgeting, could not sit still and was very, very stressed. She could not make eye contact at all. She had a very busy lifestyle, a busy and stressful job, was not eating properly and was doing too much exercise at the end of the day when she was clearly exhausted.

During her third session with me we also worked on some relaxation and I did some hypnosis with her. She became visibly relaxed and even she could feel the difference, but then she promptly burst into tears. She said she had never allowed herself to properly relax before, or even just to sit quietly and do nothing. She said that she felt guilty unless she was constantly on the go. She conceived that month and did not need the IUI.

★

Comprehensive research by Dr Alice Domar, a psychologist and a leading figure in infertility research, found that *infertile women report the same levels of anxiety and depression as women with cancer, heart disease or HIV.*[2] It is widely accepted that stress can affect the menstrual cycle and even cause cessation of the cycle altogether. If stress can cause disruptions to the menstrual cycle then surely it follows that stress must have an effect on fertility? Because a regular and normal menstrual cycle is crucial to follicle production and ovulation. Why is the diagnosis of unexplained infertility on the increase? Unexplained infertility is where there is no medical reason for the infertility. In other words, there is nothing wrong with the reproduction system of either partner! If there is nothing physically wrong then shouldn't we be looking further afield to see if there is another reason for the infertility? Do our emotions affect our reproductive system? They must do, because if we look back at what happens in the stress response the reproductive system is put on hold. We know that cortisol is produced as a result of stress and a cascade of hormones along the hypothalamus/pituitary/adrenal axis, and that this overrides the hypothalamus/pituitary/ovarian axis, which is the fertility pathway. As a result the following imbalances occur:

- Irregular menstrual cycles
- Poor follicle production and quality
- Increased cortisol prevents ovulation
- Increased cortisol also affects progesterone production, which is needed for implantation

71

- Disruption of the HPO axis causes FSH to rise
- The fight-or-flight response directs blood flow away from the reproductive system
- This leads to inadequate uterine blood flow, which could prevent implantation
- Increased prolactin, which is another hormone that can affect or prevent ovulation
- Increased risk of miscarriage

It is easy to see from this list how too much cortisol could affect fertility. Some of the conditions on the above list are used to 'diagnose' fertility problems, for example in poor follicle production and quality – a woman may be told that she's in the early menopause, particularly if the FSH levels are also high. This has been the case in so many of my patients.

★

Patient 9

This patient (age 31) came to see me a few years ago, desperate for help because she had been told that because her FSH (follicle stimulating hormone) levels were so high (58.6) that she was in early menopause. You can imagine how devastated she was at being told this by her fertility consultant. However her menstrual cycle was regular, although she did admit to being under a lot of stress while trying to conceive. She had been told that she could not have IVF as her ovaries wouldn't respond to the medication, and that she should consider having donor eggs. She was distraught.

We sat down and chatted through this diagnosis and decided that if that was the case then there was time to address the stress and anxiety in her life, as if she was having donor eggs anyway then her advancing body clock wouldn't make any difference to the outcome. We started acupuncture treatment and after a few weeks I could see a huge difference in her, she appeared calmer and less stressed, and so I suggested that when she got her next period she should get a blood test done on days one to three to measure her FSH levels again. When she text me with the result I was as ecstatic as she was – in just a few weeks her FSH had come down to 14.3; we were over the moon! The following month as she sat in my consulting room we both cried when she told me she was pregnant! After a normal and healthy pregnancy she had a beautiful baby boy. Just under two years later she conceived and gave birth to twin boys, again completely naturally.

★

What really upset and concerned me was how many other women had been given this diagnosis, which as it turned out was completely inaccurate. How many other women out there had just accepted that diagnosis and might never have their own biological child? There have been a number of patients like Patient 9 that I have seen and successfully treated.

I'm not saying that all women with similar FSH levels will have the same positive outcomes as the patient above, and I'm not criticising the medical establishment as I think they do a fantastic job, but I do think that all options should be considered (including lifestyle and stress) before patients are given such a devastating diagnosis. Many IVF clinics will not proceed with an IVF cycle if a woman has a FSH reading greater than ten because they believe the ovaries will not respond to the medication. Many clinics will abandon the cycle as happened to another of my patients.

★

Another couple came to see me who were going to have IVF due to male factor fertility issues (low sperm count). I started seeing this patient but then got a phone call from her husband explaining that they would have to cancel their next appointment because their IVF had been abandoned due to her raised FSH levels. I said '*Oh, please don't cancel her appointment; I do believe I may be able to help.*' So she continued to have acupuncture until her next period arrived and had her FSH measured again. She was delighted to inform me that her FSH had dropped from ten to eight and her IVF was going ahead that month. It was successful and they had twin girls. Just two years after that they conceived naturally and had another little girl.

★

Stress and the Cardiovascular System

It is a well-known fact that high blood pressure, heart attacks, high cholesterol and strokes are closely linked to stress. High levels of stress will trigger the fight-or-flight response. This means that in order to 'escape' the danger or perceived danger the body increases the heart rate to pump more blood into the limbs to enable us to run for our life or to fight our attacker. As discussed earlier blood is also directed away from non-essential areas such as the reproductive system, the digestive system and the immune system. In order to regulate blood flow in this way some blood vessels will be constricted or narrowed while others will become dilated and relaxed. This combined effort of narrowing and relaxing various blood vessels results in the blood pressure becoming increased during stress.

This increase in blood pressure can in turn cause damage to the lining of blood vessels which then attracts the tiny particles of sugar, fat and cholesterol which stick to the vessel walls and are the reserved 'food' for the fight-or-flight response. On top of that, the blood becomes more viscous (or thicker) and clots more easily, and the reason for this is that if we came out on the wrong side of a fight our blood would clot and the bleeding would stop.

But how does this affect fertility? Well for a start during stress blood is directed away from the reproductive system, potentially compromising the uterine lining, and secondly blood is more viscous and more prone to clotting. A large number of women I see have the same sort of pattern in their menstrual cycle – painful and very clotty periods. Should pregnancy occur then thicker, more viscous and clotty blood is not good news for an implanting embryo. It could lead to inadequate uterine blood flow which prevents implantation and could also be a factor in an increased risk of miscarriage.

*

Patient 11

When this patient (age 38) came to see me she had been trying for a family for over two years. She had conceived quite easily but had suffered five miscarriages – all of them around the five to six-week mark. She had been to a miscarriage specialist in London who couldn't find a reason why she kept losing her babies.

When I first saw her, her periods were heavy, dark and clotty as well as very painful. She was also understandably extremely anxious that when she became pregnant again she would have another miscarriage. After just two months of treatment her cycle had improved – it was lighter, less painful and much brighter in colour. She conceived in the fourth month and we continued with the sessions as well as some affirmations and visualisation. We continued right the way through the pregnancy and she went on to have a healthy baby girl.

Patient's Story:

To be honest I didn't really want to try acupuncture – I'm not a fan of needles, and I'm also more of a scientist at heart. However I was amazed at how much better I felt in myself just after the first session. I was less stressed, had much more energy, I was sleeping better and I felt altogether more positive and optimistic than I had for a long time. I couldn't believe it when my periods changed – they were less painful and there were no clots. When I found out I was pregnant this time I just knew it was going to be OK. I felt different, and I also felt calmer and less anxious. I continued to have acupuncture – which really relaxed me – right up until I was 12 weeks. It was then that I could really relax. I even continued the acupuncture once a month right the way through my pregnancy. I would definitely recommend it to anyone who is having problems becoming or staying pregnant. I also found the affirmations and visualisation very helpful and the minute I found myself starting to become negative I would say the affirmations which really helped me stay on track.

★

Stress and the Immune System

The immune system is the body's natural defence mechanism, protecting us against invading bacteria and viruses. It is made up of lymph nodes and vessels, glands such as the thymus and tonsils, white blood cells, the spleen and bone marrow.

Short periods of stress will actually increase the function of the immune system for a very short time, but it is prolonged or chronic stress and anxiety that can compromise the immune system to the extent that we are unable to fight off viruses and we become ill.

It is well known that chronic stress can lead to the shrinking of the thymus gland and a suppression of the immune system. It is also a well-known fact that cortisol also directly affects the thymus gland as well as inhibiting white blood cell production. White blood cells are designed to destroy invading pathogens and so a decreased number of white blood cells will reduce the efficiency of the immune system. Chronic stress in fact throws our immune system into chaos. Prolonged stress can in fact result in the immune system not only losing the ability to fight off pathogens, but it can also start to destroy the body's own healthy tissue resulting in allergies as well as autoimmune conditions such as multiple sclerosis, lupus, endometriosis, rheumatoid arthritis and so on.[3,4,5]

So how can a depleted immune system affect fertility? Well, as the late Allan Beer described:

The most aggressive of the immune system's fighting cells are the natural killer cells (NK cells). NK cells circulate the body looking out for cancerous or virus-infected cells – anything that fits the category of 'altered-self... NK cells contain a deadly tumour necrosis factor alpha (TNF-alpha) which kills cancer cells. Unfortunately, unregulated TNF-alpha can have a disastrous effect on every stage of reproduction, from egg quality and implantation to foetal growth and survival. So although NK cells are mostly a force for the good in regulating cell growth and protecting the body from tumours, they can also play a major role in infertility, IVF and miscarriage.[6]

If it is suspected that the cause of infertility or recurrent failed IVF cycles is due to increased levels of NK cells, then in many IVF clinics it is addressed and treated with immunotherapy. Immunotherapy is a bit of a controversial area in fertility medicine as there is little evidence to support its use, but many clinics are now resorting to that way of thinking, particularly after someone has had several failed cycles of IVF or when there is unexplained infertility, because they don't know what else to do. Isn't it about time we acknowledge that there could well be a connection between stress, the immune system and unexplained infertility?

When someone is particularly stressed, their diet, exercise regime and lifestyle issues are usually also affected – they may eat more junk food or eat for emotional reasons, they may drink more alcohol, or even smoke. As a result of these poor lifestyle choices their already depleted immune system may become compromised even further and so it becomes a vicious circle.

Stress and the Digestive System

Johann Wolfgang von Goethe, a great German writer and philosopher, believed that the gut was *the seat of all human emotions*. How often, when we are stressed out, do we say that our stomach is churning, or that we feel sick to the stomach?

The stomach has also been described by some as the second brain. When we are in fight-or-flight, blood is directed away from the digestive system because it is not essential to our survival. This then affects the way the digestive muscles work, and also has an effect on the secretions needed for digesting food. This can result in diarrhoea or the other extreme, constipation. Neither are particularly useful as essential nutrients and fluids are lost during diarrhoea and the body could become dehydrated, while with constipation harmful toxins are not excreted from the body. Both could compromise our health and as a result affect our reproduction to a greater or lesser extent. Inflammation of the gut can also result from stress, causing ulcers or infection.

As well as the effect on digestion, increased cortisol can also raise the risk of metabolic syndrome. In chronic stress, cortisol and insulin levels rise, sending messages to our fat cells to store and hold onto as much fat as possible. This means that stress actually keeps the body from releasing fat to use for energy – i.e. stress stops us losing weight. Cortisol also stimulates our appetite making us eat more, but not only that it makes us crave carbohydrates and junk food. All of this leads to weight gain, but particularly weight gain around the abdomen. It also slows down our metabolic rate and decreases our sensitivity to insulin, and reduces our levels of thyroid-stimulating hormone, growth hormone, testosterone and DHEA, all contributing to an increase in abdominal fat and increased weight.

So how can this affect fertility? Being overweight goes hand in hand with fertility problems. Abdominal fat is known to produce male hormones – androgens – which prevent the development and growth of follicles leading to anovulation and irregular menstrual cycles. It can contribute to reduced conception and response to fertility treatment such as IVF, and there is also an increased risk of miscarriage. Many women who are overweight also have polycystic ovary syndrome (PCOS). PCOS is an insulin resistant condition that causes menstrual irregularity and is believed to be directly related to obesity.

Women who have problems with obesity can greatly improve their chances of ovulating by reducing their weight by just 5%. Good nutrition, a low glycaemic index (GI) diet and exercise, together with some lifestyle changes, can make a significant difference. By adding in some techniques to reduce stress will also increase their chances of conceiving. More on this later in the book.

Stress and Depression

Chronic (long-term) stress has been linked to depression. People who are depressed tend to have higher levels of cortisol and adrenaline in their system even though they may not actually feel stressed. Depression can be caused by anxiety, extreme stress or grief, in fact any of the emotions that trigger the stress response can result in some form of depression. People who are depressed seem to be prone to black-or-white or all-or-nothing thinking, but more often than not appear to see things from a negative perspective[7]. Depression is an illness that affects every part of your life. It affects you physically – you feel exhausted and drained and can't be bothered to exercise. It affects you emotionally – you may feel constantly angry, guilty or helpless. It affects you socially – you can't face going out and meeting friends; and it affects you mentally – you can't concentrate or have difficulty making the simplest of decisions such as what to have for dinner.

Depression is an illness that is associated with a chemical imbalance and is a very real biological disease even though we can't see it. Many women feel that if they are depressed they should just pull themselves together, but it is not that simple. If you have been unable to conceive for more than three years you should consider whether you may be depressed and seek help. According to Dr Alice Domar's book *Conquering Infertility*, depression can negatively affect fertility[8], but with the right help and support it can be treated.

When making a diagnosis of depression there are nine symptoms that have to be taken into account: depressed mood, loss of interest in usual activities, loss of or increase in appetite, too much or too little sleep, feeling anxious or lethargic, lack of energy, feelings of worthlessness, inability to think straight, and feelings of death or suicide[9].

Depression can affect fertility in a number of ways:

- Depression and its related stress suppress the hormones required for ovulation
- Lowered libido means you don't feel like having sex
- Exhaustion – you're too tired for sex
- Depression affects the immune system, which means that if you are not healthy you may be less able to conceive

If you think you may be suffering from even mild depression, I urge you to see your GP as soon as possible. Depression should be treated otherwise it could lead to long-term health problems. It is easily controlled with the right support and treatment such as medication and/or psychotherapy. Another good thing is that fertility problems related to depression can be overcome. So if you think you have depression and are trying to start a family then please get some help and support before it's too late.

Stress and the Ageing Process

We've suspected for a long time that lifestyle choices can influence ageing. You only have to look at people who take recreational drugs or smoke or drink alcohol to excess to see that they appear much older than their years. Now scientists have found that chronic stress also appears to accelerate the ageing process. This could explain why long-term emotional stress can contribute to the ageing process and make us more susceptible to various illnesses.

A study published in *The Lancet Oncology* suggested that healthy lifestyle choices such as doing more exercise and eating the right foods could increase an enzyme which is essential for protecting against age-related cell damage. This enzyme is called telomerase and it repairs and lengthens telomeres, which protect the ends of our chromosomes and stops them fraying. Without telomeres, DNA strands can fray and become damaged impeding cell health and function. As we age our telomeres shorten and our cells become more susceptible to dying. Chronic stress has been found to be the telomeres' worst enemy. But it appears that a diet high in fruit, vegetables and oily fish, along with vitamin supplements and stress management, can *reverse ageing at a cellular level* according to researchers.

So if chronic stress increases ageing, can it influence fertility in the same way? Can we reverse the age of our eggs? Well no, of course we can't change the eggs we were born with, but surely by decreasing stress and adopting a healthy lifestyle we can reverse ageing at a cellular level, thereby creating a healthier environment around the developing follicles, and a healthier environment into which an embryo can implant? We know that chronic stress affects fertility in many ways as discussed earlier – interrupting our hormone levels and directing blood away from the reproductive system – and so it follows that reducing stress may help fertility in many more ways than we had originally imagined.

So chronic stress is not good news. However as we have seen above it is not just the direct effect stress has on our reproductive system that affects our fertility, but it can also be presumed that stress can also affect fertility in an indirect way by its effect on other areas of the body.

References

1. Kate Brian, *Meet The Professor, Fertility Road*, Jan/Feb 2014
2. Domar A. D. et al. *The Prevalence and Predictability of Depression in Infertile Women. Fertility and Sterility*, 58:1158–63, 1992
3. Shawn Talbott, *The Cortisol Connection*, Hunter House, Alameda, 2007
4. Cohen S, Tyrrell D. A. J. and Smith A. P. *Psychological Stress and Susceptibility to the Common Cold. The New England Journal of Medicine*, 1991, Volume 325:606–612
5. McLeod, S. A. (2010) *Stress, Illness and the Immune System.* Retrieved from http://www.simplypsychology.org/stress-immune.html
6. Alan E. Beer MD, *Is Your Body Baby Friendly?* AJR Publishing 2006, p29
7. Joe Griffin and Ivan Tyrrell, *How to Lift Depression Fast*, HG Publishing, Great Britain, 2004
8. Alice D. Domar*, Conquering Infertility: Dr Alice Domar's Mind/ Body Guide to Enhancing Fertility and Coping with Infertility*, New York, 2002
9. Joe Griffin and Ivan Tyrrell, *How to Lift Depression Fast*, HG Publishing, Great Britain, 2004

Chapter Five

Take Control

Every woman who heals herself helps heal all the women who came before her, and all those who came after her.
Christine Northrup MD, *Mother-Daughter Wisdom*

Now that we understand a bit about our emotions and how our emotions and feelings can create psychological stress within the body, we can do something about it. Taking control of your emotions and your fertility means an end to feeling helpless. It will take a little bit of self-discipline like any self-help programme, but taking control is incredibly empowering.

Stress seems to be the new buzzword and almost weekly over the past few months I have come across published articles on managing stress, mindfulness, spreading yourself too thinly, advice for frazzled, rushing women, and so it goes on! What is this telling us about the society we're living in? Is it a sign of the times; a reflection on the way everyone is living their lives, busier than ever and stressed out? Is this way of life contributing to the increasing number of people who are obese, or suffering from cardiovascular disease, or being diagnosed with cancer or fertility problems? In their book *The Healing Code*, Alexander Loyd and Ben Johnson state that *the one thing that just about everyone does agree on is that almost all health issues originate from one problem – STRESS!*[1]

As we said earlier you may not *feel* stressed out and so please do not think you have done anything wrong, because you haven't – this is not your fault. This is the 21st century. The car needs a service, there's a train strike, the boiler breaks down and then the last straw is that you get your period – all these things are sent to try us, they are stressful and challenge us in our day-to-day lives and they are unavoidable, but they are not your fault. However they are enough to drive us to the brink of distraction! There is a biological reason for feeling the way you do and so you should not feel guilty. It is easy to influence and change that biology with things that you can do yourself. What I can do through this book is show you how to manage and cope with these events in your life so that they don't end up stressing you out and impacting on your health or fertility. In fact the techniques I describe are based on research that shows that by reducing that internal stress you can indeed increase your chances of becoming pregnant.

The self-help techniques in this book are designed specifically for you to do, and in your own time. Self-help systems are very powerful because you are in control. Knowledge is power and it can be extremely satisfying to be doing something for yourself. It is not only very empowering but also has a strong placebo effect. The knowledge and belief that you are doing something to help yourself brings about many physiological changes in the body.

The good news is that there are almost as many ways of dealing with stress and our rollercoaster of emotions as there are things that cause those feelings of being helpless and out of control. There are healthy ways to cope with stress, but they all require change – a change in the situation, or in your reaction to that situation. You may have to learn to accept and or adapt your view of life or the situation, e.g.

- Don't try to control the uncontrollable
- Look for the upside
- Share your feelings with your partner, a family member or a close friend

85

- Learn to forgive
- Let go of anger and resentment
- Let go of all negative energy by doing activities that are positive and make you laugh

The aim of this book is to give you a choice of remedies that suit you, that fit in with your lifestyle and are realistic and easy to do, and above all, are not going to cost the earth! In fact the majority of these solutions are actually free! Yes, free!

So what are the solutions available to us?

Manage Your Stress

First of all you need to establish which area of your life is causing you stress. Is it work-related stress, is it because your life is so busy and there are literally not enough hours in the day, or is it the stress of trying to get pregnant? Is the stress a product of your thoughts – are you a born worrier or generally an anxious person? Perhaps your stress is caused by terrible grief. Have you suffered a tragic loss or bereavement? Have you lost a family member or close friend, or perhaps suffered a miscarriage or stillbirth? Maybe you are angry with someone or something or are fearful of losing your job, or have money worries. Are you the major breadwinner and perhaps concerned about how you and your partner will manage when you are on maternity leave? Perhaps it is a combination of several of these things. Whatever the reason, once you have acknowledged that's what the problem is, it is possible to find a solution.

Work Stress

If you are finding work stressful, why not see if you can work from home for a couple of days a week instead? People who work from home find that they get more done as they are not distracted by phone calls and colleagues. According to a survey carried out by the University of California, office workers are interrupted from their task every 11 minutes and then spend even more time recovering from the distractions. If however you do work from home even for a day or so, you must make sure that your work doesn't spill over into your 'home' time! Have a designated work area or office space and only work from there. When not in that area, do not think about work and resist checking your emails. Only work in the time that you've allocated yourself for work – don't be tempted to work overtime just because you are working from home! If you end up working into your own time you will only become more frustrated and resentful with your job and yourself. So be kind to yourself and your work by 'turning work off' – turn off your work phone/BlackBerry/computer so that you actually find time that really is your own without any interruptions. Technology today means that we are available 24/7 and unless you are a doctor on call, surely nothing is that urgent that it can't wait until the next day.

If you are a career woman then maybe you have tried to plan out your life, including the best time to become pregnant and have a baby. Now you feel even more frustrated than ever because infertility is interfering with your plans. Perhaps you are feeling guilty because you are missing work to attend various hospital appointments, or perhaps because you are working too hard and are unable to devote enough time to your fertility. Perhaps you no longer get job satisfaction like you used to because now all you want is to be a mum. Perhaps you are thinking of giving up your job to devote more time to IVF, but then again you may be stressed that by giving up your job you may not be able to afford IVF. Or are you not particularly happy in your job and can't wait to get pregnant so that you can go on maternity leave and then leave altogether? All these things just seem to impact on your stress levels even more. There is no right or wrong answer

– you have to do what feels more comfortable for you. What I can help you with is putting everything into perspective, feeling more positive and teaching you some relaxation techniques to carry you through this phase in your life. Because it is just a phase and like all phases, this too will pass.

Is Your Fertility Causing You Stress?

We now know from recent research that stress causes infertility, but we also know that infertility causes a huge amount of stress and despair. Infertility is not simply a physical problem and our feelings and emotions such as fear, grief and anxiety are all major factors in this complex process.

Someone who has been unlucky to experience a miscarriage is naturally going to feel anxious in case it should happen again. The woman who is approaching her mid-30s will have read articles about age affecting fertility and may be worrying about not being able to get pregnant even before she starts trying. In fact many of my patients are panicking in case they can't get pregnant, even before they start to try, such is the influence of the media and social networks. Someone with unexplained infertility is going to feel frustrated that doctors haven't been able to find the cause of her infertility. The poor woman who has been told by her doctor that her FSH is so high that donor eggs are the only answer is going to feel distraught at that diagnosis – she may feel helpless, guilty or even a failure, and even though it may not be completely true, all these factors play a huge part in our emotions and our hormonal balance. By following some of the self-help techniques in this book you will be able to understand and control your emotions more easily, and should feel more positive about the whole process. Recognising what is causing the way you are feeling is half the battle.

Are you a multi-tasker? Women are notorious for multi-tasking, but as Steve Uzzell states, *Multi-tasking is merely the opportunity to screw up more than one thing at a time.*[2] What this means is that although it is possible to do two things at once such as walking and talking, it is virtually impossible to actually *focus* on two things at once. Trying to focus on two things at once leads to mistakes being made. This is why it is now illegal to use a mobile phone whilst driving a car, it causes a distraction and lack of concentration. Trying to do two or more things at a time when we have a lot to do is a common complaint because we believe we can get things done faster. Sometimes when we have so much on our plate it is difficult to know where to begin. I think many of us have been in a situation where there is so much to do and we are so overwhelmed that we procrastinate and waste so much time panicking about where to start that nothing gets done! Make a list and stick to it! Better still, say NO to things and people – look after number one! If you are a hard worker and conscientious then you will be asked to help out more than most people. Don't be afraid to say no! Don't overcommit yourself.

Sometimes it is an accumulation of little things that cause us to become stressed and drag us down, such as a button that needs sewing on, a form that needs filling in, a pile of paperwork that needs filing; a cupboard that needs sorting out or returning that phone call. Make a list of all the little things that need to be done and gradually work through the list ticking them off one by one – you will feel so much better when they are done and dusted and you are not worrying about them. By working your way through your list and tackling one thing at a time each job will get done, which is much better than having lots of half-finished jobs.

Gary Keller and Jay Papasan, in their book *The One Thing*, say:

> *It's not that we have too little time to do all the things we need to do, it's that we feel the need to do too many things in the time we have. So we double and triple up in the hope of getting everything done.*[3]

How true is that? I'm sure we've all been there – we have a few minutes to spare before going to work and so instead of leaving then and there and taking our time and getting to work a few minutes early feeling calm and relaxed, we decide to put some washing on or hang the washing out, or empty the dishwasher etc. When we eventually leave a little later than planned and then get stuck in traffic our stress levels soar and we wonder why we arrive late and stressed!

Think of ways of saving time such as shopping online – almost anything can be bought online these days without the hassle of taking a trip into town, finding somewhere to park and so on. Is your home a museum? Stress can be caused by having too much clutter all around us! De-junk and take a trip to the charity shop or sell things online if you have time. You will feel so much better when your home is organised

Manage Your Thoughts – Change the Way You Think!

Our body is the product of our thoughts. We're beginning to understand in medical science the degree to which the nature of our thoughts and emotions actually determines the physical substance and structure and function of our bodies.
Dr John Hagelin, quantum physicist and public policy expert[4]

When people are completely focused on what's wrong and their symptoms, they will perpetuate it. The healing will not occur until they shift their attention from being sick to being well. Because that's the Law of Attraction.
Bob Doyle[5]

Are you constantly focused on your fertility and your monthly cycle, living from one day to the next thinking about nothing else? One of my patients was so obsessed with her basal body temperature (BBT) charts that she used to check them obsessively 20 times a day! Deepak Chopra says in his book *Perfect Health* that *people who worry excessively about disease fall prey to it more often.*[6] Try to manage those thoughts by writing down all the positive things you are doing to take control of your fertility. As you read on through the book you will find lots of self-help tips such as breathing, relaxation techniques, visualisation and mindfulness that can help you through the difficult days and make you feel positive about the way you are managing your fertility and your emotions.

Complaining

Try not to moan or complain. By complaining, blaming, finding fault or criticising someone or something you are not getting something off your chest, you are just creating more bad feeling and more negative energy. When you complain about the weather or being kept waiting for an appointment, heavy traffic or a poor meal in a restaurant, you are only intensifying those bad feelings. Change the way you think and speak and try not to use negative words such as *terrible, horrible, disgusting* and *awful*, which carry such strong negative feelings. When you use them they will only make you feel bad-tempered and depressed. Try to go through life without being judgemental, without only looking at the negative aspects – there is usually a reason for everything. When you are stuck in traffic think about the poor person who has broken down or been in a car accident – it's not their fault and they are in a much worse position than you. They didn't want to cause a traffic jam. If its road works think about how much better the roads will be as a result of the resurfacing! Use the time spent waiting to practise some deep breathing – there's nothing you can do about it so stop fretting and use the time to your advantage! There is blue sky above every cloud so try to look on the bright side of every eventuality and try to incorporate words like *amazing, fantastic, wonderful* and *brilliant* into your everyday speech. You will be amazed by how much better you feel for it.

When we think positively we don't activate the stress response; instead we feel calm and relaxed. But when we think negative thoughts, we go into fight-or-flight mode. Our thoughts transform into our feelings, and our feelings into physical effects in the body. If a woman is trying to get pregnant but is immersed in negative thoughts most of the time what message is that sending to her body?

> *Nothing comes from without. All things come from within.*
> Neville Goddard (1905–1972), *New Thought* author

Our cells are listening! Professor William Tiller, a physicist at Stanford University, has produced a device that measures electromagnetic energy. He subsequently came across an energy field not in the electromagnetic spectrum and was able to demonstrate that this energy field responded to human intention. The energy field behaved differently when faced with negative thoughts compared with positive ones.[7] Another expert in mind-body medicine, Candace Pert, said, *your mind is in every cell in your body.*[8]

There is now scientific evidence to show that the way we think can really impact on the cells and systems of our body. Biologists now know that our cells are constantly changing and at the same time are responding and reacting to the environment surrounding them. This environment includes the air that we breathe, the food we eat, the water we drink, the influence of people around us and also our emotions – our thoughts and beliefs. Research from Massachusetts discovered that each cell has a receptor on its surface which allows it to communicate with the surrounding environment. The receptors then tell the cells what functions they should be performing.[9]

We now know that our cells are reacting and responding to everything we do – eating, drinking, our thoughts, exercise and so on. As a result the information within our cells can have a profound effect on our physiology, including our hormones, our circulation and our immune system – all of which affect our fertility. Our cells are also constantly being renewed and replaced as old cells die. Our skin cells are continually being replaced and our hair and nails are constantly growing.

Deepak Chopra in his book *Perfect Health* explains:

A typical cell in the lining of our stomach lives only a few days, a typical skin cell only two weeks; a red blood cell will live for two or three months while those long-lived cells in the liver take longer to replace themselves.[10]

How amazing is that? If we are continually replacing parts of our body surely this gives hope to women with problems like endometriosis or PCOS? Food for thought!

So how does all this science apply to the woman trying to get pregnant? Well it means that the body is constantly changing and our thoughts, beliefs and attitudes can have an influence on our cells, on our physiology and on our ability to become pregnant. Our thoughts and beliefs have a profound effect on what is actually happening in our body. The way we think affects our cells and so being optimistic really can improve your outcome and your health. A study in Ohio in 2007 concluded that optimists responded well to treatment that they believed could help them.

The key to healing really does come from within us. People who worry constantly about their health are prone to becoming sick more often.[11] This is often known as health anxiety. So many of my patients worry excessively about their fertility even before they start trying for a baby, and the biggest thing they worry about is that they won't be able to get pregnant because they worry that they have left it too late.

Rhonda Byrne, in her book *The Magic*, says,

> *When there is some kind of sickness or condition in your body, it is understandable that you may have negative feelings about it, like worry, frustration or fear. But having negative feelings about sickness does not restore health. In fact, it has the opposite effect – it reduces health even more. To increase health, you need to replace the negative feelings with good feelings.*[12]

So when you are constantly thinking about your fertility, worrying about it or feeling frustrated because you can't control it, this is actually not going to help. However if you think about all the positive things that you are doing to improve your health, your lifestyle and your fertility, such as practising relaxation or mindfulness, eating healthily or doing some exercise, then those will generate positive feelings which *will* actually help. Keep a list of all the positive things that you are doing, then when you have a 'down' day read the list to remind yourself of all the good things you are doing. This will help to keep you more positive and optimistic about the outcome.

References

1. Alexander Loyd and Ben Johnson, *The Healing Code*, Hodder and Stoughton, London, 2011

2. Steve Uzzell, as cited by Gary Keller and Jay Papasan in *The One Thing*, John Murray, London, 2013, p44

3. Gary Keller and Jay Papasan, *The One Thing*, John Murray, London, 2013, p46

4. Dr John Hagelin, as cited in Rhonda Byrne, *The Secret*, Simon and Schuster UK Ltd, 2006, p125

5. Bob Doyle, as cited in Rhonda Byrne, *The Secret,* Simon and Schuster UK Ltd, 2006, p132

6. Deepak Chopra, *Perfect Health*, Bantam Books, Great Britain, 2001, p9

7. Donna Eden, *Energy Medicine*, Piatkus, London, 2008

8. Candace Pert, *Molecules of Emotion: Why You Feel the Way you Feel*, New York, Scribner, 1997

9. James Schwartz, *The Mind-Body Fertility Connection*, Llewellyn Publications, Minnesota, 2008

10. Deepak Chopra, *Perfect Health*, Bantam Books, Great Britain, 2001, p24

11. Deepak Chopra, *Perfect Health*, Bantam Books, Great Britain, 2001

12. Rhonda Byrne, *The Magic*, Simon and Schuster UK Ltd, 2012, p150

Chapter Six

Self-help Techniques

In this chapter I want to show you some techniques that you can do for yourself to help reduce the effects of stress on the body. The techniques are simple to do and cost nothing and yet they are so effective in reducing the stress response and promoting relaxation, while at the same time increasing circulation and improving the immune system as well as a host of other health benefits. By following the advice and practising the ensuing techniques you really can make a difference to your fertility.

Breathing

Just by focusing on our breathing we can lower our stress levels immediately. We take one breath after another without giving it a second thought because it is an automatic reaction and it doesn't occur to us that there is always enough air for us to breathe! As we breathe oxygen enters our body through our lungs and then gets absorbed into our red blood cells and travels through our bloodstream, feeding every single cell so that we can continue to live. This essential life-sustaining action is something we all take for granted and we only really appreciate it when we can't catch our breath, or if we have a cough or cold or suffer from asthma.

We can however control our breathing to some extent. Breathing is the only autonomic response in the body that we have some control over. We can't physically control our heart beating, our last meal being digested or our blood pressure. But we can to an extent control our breathing. We can all hold our breath for a certain period of time – some people longer than others – and we can all slow our breathing down or breathe faster. We have the ability to take really deep breaths or to breathe more shallowly. Everyone at some time in their life has experienced that feeling when you can't catch your breath – this is usually when we are feeling very stressed. People who have panic attacks have difficulty breathing in, as do people who have asthma attacks. Breathing into a paper bag for both these problems helps because breathing in the carbon dioxide that we normally breathe out helps to trigger our in-breath again!

Controlling our breathing can help us to have some control over our emotions. We've all heard the phrase 'hold your breath and count to ten' before you react when you are angry. By controlling and slowing down our breathing we can in fact control the stress response.

Physiological changes happen in the body when we are able to control our breathing and these changes are particularly effective when we slow our breathing right down. To really get the hang of it, sit or lie down somewhere comfortable to begin with. Once you grasp the technique it can be done anywhere. Place your hands on your abdomen and as you take a breath in, push your tummy out against your hands – this takes some getting used to because as women we have a tendency to pull our tummy in!

Continue to breathe in through your nose, feeling that tummy rise under your hands, and then out through your mouth. Do this several more times. Pushing your tummy out means that you are using your diaphragm properly when you breathe. As your tummy rises your diaphragm lowers and this expands the chest even more, and so you are using all of your lung space to get air in. This means that much more oxygen is getting into your lungs and consequently into your bloodstream and your tissues. When we are stressed we tend to breathe with only the upper part of our lungs and so tend to breathe much more shallowly. Also, we tend to sigh and yawn more as our body strives to get more oxygen into our tissues. Once you have mastered this diaphragmatic breathing you can control your breathing even further. Breathe in through your nose to a count of three, and then out through your mouth to a count of six. When you've mastered this you can breathe in to four and out to eight, or in to five and out to ten, whichever is more comfortable for you. The important things to remember are:

- The abdomen rises each time, i.e. you are using your diaphragm to breathe
- The out-breath is longer than the in-breath

When the out-breath is longer this will trigger the parasympathetic nervous system, which is the relaxation response; the opposite of fight-or-flight. This is exactly what we want because when we are relaxed more blood is directed towards our reproductive system, and there is more oxygen and increased circulation to our tissues. Our blood pressure drops and so does our heart rate. This 3/6 or 4/8 diaphragmatic breathing can be done anywhere and at any time. It can be done just for relaxation at the start of meditation or visualisation or when we are stressed or overwhelmed. It can be done in the car if you are stuck in traffic, in work if things are piling on top of you, in a meeting or even when a colleague or friend announces she is pregnant. Remember by controlling your breathing you can help control your emotions. Breathe in peace and calm, and with the longer out-breath, breathe out anger, frustration and stress. Breath in peace and calm, breathe out anger, frustration and stress.

Our lifestyles today are very busy and complicated and filled with a vast array of distractions. Even when we do have some time to relax we tend to switch on the television, or watch a film on our tablet and subject our brains to a multitude of changing images and sounds. We are so used to being stimulated from the outside that we find it difficult to relax and do nothing. When do we enjoy the stillness of our own minds? Cleansing the mind is like removing all the stones and weeds from the garden before we sow the seeds. If we don't do this our minds will remain polluted by negative thoughts past and present and unless we remove them they will obstruct future growth and development.[1]

So many of the patients I see have no control over their minds. They can't seem to relax and just do nothing. They can't concentrate, are constantly tired, lack energy and are often ill with colds and viruses. They often see the world in a negative light, complaining about the weather, traffic, poor service and so on. What we have to remember is that above all those black clouds the sky is still blue. When you relax and quieten the mind all those black clouds will soon pass, revealing the blue sky that was there all the time, hidden, just like the quiet of our mind is hidden by the thousands of thoughts we have every day. By spending some time doing some relaxation or mindfulness we allow our brain to rest and recover from the busy lifestyles in our modern world. The 21st century is a frantic place and there are demands not only on our time but also our senses, which creates stress.

Doing the breathing exercises in this book is an excellent way to relax, as are meditation, doing some gentle yoga or just reading a lighthearted book or even a magazine where you can spend a few quiet minutes just relaxing. I ask my patients to spend a few minutes every day having a little 'luxury'. This could be relaxing with a book or magazine or catching up with a good friend for a cuppa and a chat. It might mean having a relaxing bath or having your nails done. Whatever you choose to do, try to do something every single day, even if it is for only 10 or 15 minutes, just to chill out. Stop feeling guilty because you'll find that as you take time out for yourself and nurture yourself, you will become more constructive in other areas of your life and so a little luxury every day is time well spent.

Read the following relaxation technique and either record it so you can listen back to it while you relax or get your partner to read it to you while you put your feet up.

Gently close your eyes and allow your body and mind to move from the outside world to your deep inner world. This is your time. As you allow yourself to become so comfortable there, there is nothing at all for you to do except to lie there and relax.

I want you to think about the top of your head. Many people don't realise that tension often starts in the little muscles of the scalp, so think about those muscles and just allow them to let go and relax. Now think about the muscles of your face and just allow them to let go and relax; your forehead, your eyes and your eyelids, your cheeks, mouth and jaw muscles, just allowing them to let go and relax. You may find that your mouth relaxes and opens slightly, but whatever is comfortable for you, just allow it to happen. Unclenching your teeth and relaxing your tongue, because the more you can physically relax, the more you can mentally relax.

Thinking about your neck and shoulder muscles now, and moving down into the tops of your arms, just letting all those muscles relax and let go. Moving down through your elbows and into your forearms, down through your wrists and into your hands and all the way down into the tips of your fingers and tips of your thumbs, just allowing all those muscles to relax and let go. Think about those muscles in your back now, those long muscles either side of your spine, just allow those muscles to relax and let go. Moving down to your abdomen now and into your hips and down into your thighs, thinking about all those muscles and feeling them let go and relax. As you move down into your legs through your knees and calf muscles, down through your ankles and into your feet, all the way down into the tips of your toes, all the muscles of your body are now beautifully relaxed. All the tension has gone and you can feel a warmth and a heaviness and tingling spreading throughout your body as you feel yourself becoming lighter and lighter and more and more relaxed as the sensation of peace and tranquillity spreads through you.

We are all different and what one person does to relax may not be suitable for another. So find a way to relax that suits you and try to spend some time every day just chilling out.

Sleep

A good night's sleep is crucial to our wellbeing. We've all had the experience of a 'bad night' when we either couldn't get to sleep because of our overthinking brain, or we woke up in the early hours and couldn't get back to sleep again. The importance of a good night's sleep cannot be overemphasised – it not only improves our mood, but boosts our energy and helps decrease stress and levels of the stress hormone cortisol. When we sleep we also produce serotonin and dopamine that boost our mood during the day. One of the best ways to reduce stress is to make sure you have adequate sleep. However, how many of us actually do the opposite? When you are juggling all the 101 things you have to do during the day, cutting down on sleep to fit in that last report or finishing marking homework or exam papers may seem like a good idea at the time. However losing even a small amount of sleep puts stress on so many aspects of our health and we now know that adequate sleep is as important as nutrition and exercise for our health and wellbeing. Lack of sleep actually affects our quality of life. It can lead to weight gain, heart disease and increased stress levels; it affects our mood, our creativity and our energy, as well as our ability to make decisions.

Most adults regularly need between seven and a half and nine hours of sleep at night. Getting less than this means you could be sleep deprived. Lack of sleep will result in:

- Feeling irritable and bad-tempered
- Feeling stressed
- Lack of creativity and imagination
- Reduced immune function and frequently becoming unwell
- Poor concentration and memory
- Weight gain
- Difficulty in making decisions
- Poor motor skills and increased risk of accidents
- Increased risk of heart disease
- Insulin resistance, leading to risk of diabetes

There are two types of sleep:

- Non-REM sleep – there are three phases, N1, N2 and N3, each deeper than the last
- REM (rapid eye movement) sleep; this is our dreaming sleep

However it's not just the amount of sleep that's important to our health and wellbeing; it's the quality of sleep that's important. N1 sleep only lasts about five minutes and is the transition into sleep. N2 is light sleep; eye movement stops, our heart rate slows down and our body temperature decreases. N3 is the deepest and most important part of sleeping because it's during this phase of sleep that the body repairs and rejuvenates. During deep sleep the body stimulates growth and development, boosts the immune system and repairs muscles and tissues.[2]

REM sleep is when we dream and our mind consolidates all our thought processes during the day. REM sleep is when we move things from our emotional brain into our intellectual brain, i.e. all our worries and stresses are processed. REM sleep also forms neural connections to improve memory and learning, and produces neurotransmitters – serotonin and dopamine – that help boost our mood during the day.

Getting enough sleep though is easier said than done when there are so many demands on your time, but you must learn not to compromise on your sleep. In order to help you establish a pattern and a good night's sleep I've put together some useful tips to help you:

- Try to get to bed at the same time each night, and to wake up at the same time each day – even on weekends
- Don't exercise within three hours before bed
- Try to avoid all stimulants late at night – you're probably avoiding most alcohol and caffeine anyway
- Try not to have any technology at all in your bedroom – ban the television and laptop and your phone!
- Treat yourself to a good old-fashioned alarm clock to wake you instead!
- Don't eat or work late at night, but do have a cup of calming camomile tea!
- Wind down in the hour before bed; try to do something calming – maybe this is a good time for meditation or visualisation

Exercise

Health professionals are still unable to agree on whether exercise is beneficial in women who are struggling to conceive. Some professionals ask women to stop exercising altogether. However exercise doesn't have to be excessive or even that strenuous, and like most things in our lives exercise in moderation is good for you. Much has been said about exercise and fertility, but is any of it proven? I agree wholeheartedly that excessive exercise when you are trying for a baby is not a good thing because it causes the body to produce adrenaline which is then seen as a stressor. The body can't tell the difference between stress from too much exercise and stress from a life-threatening situation and so ends up in fight-or-flight mode. But that is *excessive* exercise – exercise in moderation is in fact a good thing. We all feel better after exercise and research shows that after exercise we actually feel better about ourselves.

So what do we mean by exercise? Exercise can be defined as *any bodily activity that enhances or maintains physical fitness and overall health and wellbeing.*[3] Regular and moderate amounts of exercise have been shown to boost the immune system and there is evidence to show it can prevent many diseases such as heart disease and cardiovascular disease. It is thought that the benefits of exercise are brought about through the action of skeletal muscle, which is in fact classed as an endocrine organ. When muscles contract they produce chemicals called myokines. Myokines are thought to help with tissue growth and repair, to help maintain healthy body functioning and also help to reduce inflammation in the body. We already know that exercise reduces the level of the stress hormone cortisol, which as we've seen earlier in the book causes a great many health problems.

There are many ways that exercise can be beneficial to our health. We were born to move! Our ancestors got rid of the excess cortisol in their bodies by running away from danger –

the problem we have in this day and age is that we can't just run away from that traffic jam or that meeting! As Ratey and Hagerman say in their book *Spark*, *If you get stressed at work would you slap your boss or turn and run for your life?*[4] Certainly not, and so exercise is today's way of getting rid of that excess cortisol and adrenaline flying around our bodies. It helps to control both the physical feelings of stress such as palpitations, knots in the stomach or insomnia, as well as the emotional feelings such as being out of control, feelings of anxiety or constant worrying.

Research has found that exercise may help to reduce pre-menstrual syndrome (PMS) and a survey of 1,800 women who used exercise to decrease PMS found that they not only had less period pain but also that their mood, concentration and erratic behaviour had improved.[5] In Chinese medicine when someone is stressed we say that their *Qi* or energy is stuck or stagnant. Exercise helps to increase the flow of *Qi* in the body, restoring balance.

So how can moderate exercise help with fertility problems? Well for a start exercise reduces stress and we know that stress can affect fertility. Exercise makes us feel happier and better about ourselves, and also helps to prevent depression. We know from research by Alice Domar that depression can cause infertility so preventing depression is a good thing for preserving our fertility and our general health. Exercise produces endorphins – the feel-good hormones which make us feel better and more motivated to do things. When we exercise with friends or in a sports centre, it means that we keep in touch with people and these social connections are also important in maintaining our mood.

Exercise gives the immune system a boost, thus helping to prevent disease and inflammation in the body. Moderate exercise strengthens the cardiovascular system by reducing blood pressure and improving blood flow, including to the reproductive organs. Exercise helps to regulate insulin in the body and may therefore help prevent metabolic syndrome such as PCOS. And for those people who are overweight, exercise helps with obesity by reducing the appetite as well as burning calories. When women have weight-related ovulation problems and irregular menstrual cycles, just reducing their weight by 5% can restore ovulation and regulate periods.

And finally, exercise helps with neuroplasticity and neurogenesis, which basically is the regeneration of brain cells. These changes help us to manage our emotions as well as increase our memory and ability to learn. And of course, exercise may help prevent us ageing too quickly. In a study we talked about earlier regarding stress and ageing, part of the healthy lifestyle undertaken by the men in the study was walking for 30 minutes six days a week. The result was that the healthy lifestyle group had longer telomeres on their chromosomes which prevented the fraying of their DNA, which in effect is reducing or delaying the effects of ageing.

Exercise can be fun and when we are happy and relaxed we can't worry or be sad at the same time. Exercise preferably means getting out and about in the fresh air and meeting people. Most people think of exercise as slogging away on the treadmill in the gym, but it doesn't need to be like that at all. So what form of exercise is good, then, for women trying to conceive? Well any exercise is good provided it is in moderation and that means roughly three or four times a week for 30 minutes, depending on the exercise of course. Keen sailors, because of the practicality of the sport may spend a whole day involved with sailing, whereas I would most definitely not recommend that you pound the streets running for the same amount of time, and so everything is relative to the sport or activity that you enjoy. And that's the crucial point – you should enjoy the exercise otherwise you will be putting yourself under more pressure and it will be counterproductive.

Try some new activities for a change, maybe kayaking, rock climbing, hill walking, golf, tennis, badminton, swimming, mountain biking, cycling, netball, hockey or dancing to name just a few. The important thing is that whatever you do should be fun. Try something new and do it just for fun and you'll soon start to feel much more relaxed, and will start to look forward to it. So many of my patients have become isolated from their friends because they have stopped going to the gym and have stopped socialising because they are avoiding alcohol and coffee and are careful with what they eat – which is a good thing, but it means that these women then become lonely and depressed because they are missing out on these social occasions. If they then stop exercising, again they are withdrawing from society and one of the advantages of exercising can be the social aspect of it. So get out there in the fresh air, drink in that sunshine and vitamin D – so crucial for fertility – and have a game of tennis or a walk along the beach or in the countryside; it will do you more good than you realise.

The latest craze to reduce stress in Japan is something called Shinrin-yoku or forest bathing! This is literally walking in woodlands and has become the latest way to reduce stress. Walking through the woods while breathing in all those woody scents is thought to be as good as natural aromatherapy. Recent studies have concluded that escaping the hustle and bustle of city life to spend time in the country is good for us and improves our physical, emotional and mental health and wellbeing. It has been shown to lower our stress hormone cortisol. Further studies showed that forest bathing increased vigour and decreased anxiety, depression and anger, suggesting that forest bathing may help reduce the risk of psychosocial stress-related diseases. So take a walk in the woods, wander through the trees, touch the leaves and the bark, listen to the birds, breathe in those woody scents, relax, reflect and heal.

It is quite possible to leave your home for a walk in the early morning air and return a different person – beguiled, enchanted.
Mary Ellen Chase (1887–1973), educator and writer

Walking anywhere however is good for you and even if you do not live near the countryside, walking is still beneficial and it's easy to do either on your own or with your partner or a group of friends. It's free and needs nothing other than suitable shoes, comfortable clothing and maybe a bottle of water. In fact walking near water will do as much good as walking in the country or in a park – water has such a calming effect whether it is a river, stream, lake or the sea; even just sitting beside a pond can still do you a power of good. Walking mindfully will reduce stress even further (see the chapter on mindfulness later in the book).

Other forms of exercise that are beneficial to fertility are yoga, Pilates, Qigong and tai chi. These cost nothing if you do them at home with the help of a DVD, however if you go to classes then they will incur a cost, but because they are usually group sessions the cost is generally small.

Yoga – Revitalising the Spirit

Yoga has been practised for around 6,000 years and although it is essentially a spiritual science it can lead to a sense of physical and emotional wellbeing. Yoga offers a spiritual approach to the physical, mental, emotional and spiritual fitness of the body. Research shows that regular yoga practice has been found to increase chemical messengers in the brain such as GABA. Some scientists believe that GABA controls the emotions such as fear and anxiety that are experienced when our neurons or nerve cells are overexcited. There is evidence to suggest that yoga may decrease blood pressure and it is used as a mind-body technique to reduce stress. It can also increase emotional stability, mental clarity and stamina. Yoga has a profound effect on the areas of the brain which govern processes such as digestion, heart rate and the production of hormones, all of which are affected by our emotions. This is what makes yoga so different from other forms of exercise. There are many different forms of yoga but hatha yoga, which is a combination of breathing, exercise and meditation, has been found to be particularly useful for fertility problems. Many of my patients really enjoy yoga because it gives them a way to reconnect with their body and it also helps them slow down a busy mind. The advantage with yoga is that anyone can practise it even if they are out of shape, are not used to doing any form of exercise or are nursing an injury. If you haven't practised yoga before it is probably better to go to a class rather than start on your own, although once you are familiar with the technique and the postures then there is no harm doing it at home in the comfort of your own living room with the help of a yoga video.

Pilates

It is the mind itself that shapes the body.

Joseph H. Pilates

Pilates is similar to yoga in that it is a mind–body form of exercise. Pilates, as the name suggests, was created by a German called Joseph Pilates who developed a series of exercises designed to strengthen the mind and body because he believed that mental and physical health were related. Pilates exercises are designed to be thoughtful, combining mental and physical techniques to develop a strong mind and body. It encourages core strength and stability. Pilates needs your full concentration, thus enabling you to be in control of every movement. The Pilates method of exercise teaches you to be in control of your body and not at its mercy. This may be helpful to some women when struggling to conceive because it is a way to reconnect with their body, giving them confidence and control.

Qigong

Qigong translated literally means 'life energy cultivation'.[6] It is a form of Traditional Chinese Medicine which involves controlled breathing techniques; slow, gentle, rhythmic movement and focused thought or meditation. Qigong is becoming increasingly popular as an important form of complementary medicine. It has been found to reduce stress, calm the mind, enhance the immune system and improve circulation. Qigong has a positive effect on both physical and emotional health and it can be practised anywhere – indoors or out – and no special equipment is needed. Qigong is another excellent exercise for women wanting to conceive.

Tai Chi

Tai chi was originally developed in China in the 13th century as a martial art but it is now recognised worldwide as a health-promoting exercise. Tai chi is a gentle activity combining deep breathing and relaxation with gentle movements. The exercise involves lots of free-flowing, easy movements that don't put stress on the body. Studies have shown that tai chi can reduce stress, and reducing stress levels will help increase chances of conception.

Meditation

Meditation is not a way of making your mind quiet. It's a way of entering into the quiet that's already there buried under the 50,000 thoughts the average person thinks every day.

Deepak Chopra

The research that I mentioned earlier regarding meditation reducing biological age, as well as increasing levels of DHEA in people who used meditation on a regular basis, is as good a reason as any to practise meditation for fertility. Meditation is an ancient form of focused thought or prayer which has been developed from Taoism in China and Buddhism in India. Meditation is a state of focused awareness in which we turn our attention to our inner being. To promote health and wellbeing we need to allow our brain to rest, and we do that by clearing the mind of any thoughts by doing meditation.

Many things in life are beyond our control, however with meditation it is possible to take responsibility for and change one's state of mind. Meditation is a means of transforming the mind. It is a technique that encourages and develops concentration, clarity and emotional positivity, and is used to achieve a calm and positive state of mind in which you are always aware of your surroundings.

To practise meditation find a place where you can sit comfortably and quietly and without being disturbed. Try to sit upright with good postural alignment if you can, or if you prefer, supported in a comfortable chair. Now focus on your breathing, taking slow, even breaths, breathing in through your nose and sighing out through your mouth. Some people focus on saying a word or phrase, others prefer to focus on a spot on the wall or on a picture. Any distractions are ignored and any thoughts or feelings should be allowed to come and go freely without spending any time thinking on them. Gradually the mind becomes quieter and the brain begins to rest, and then the deeper levels of relaxation are reached. When this happens, the body physically begins to change, and our sympathetic nervous system – our fight-or-flight – switches off and heart rate and blood pressure falls as the body and mind reaches a state of inner peace and calm, and deep relaxation and improved health. In his book *Timeless Healing: The Power and Biology of Belief*, Herbert

Benson describes the relaxation response as *silencing the chaos within*.[7] Meditation is not about trying to quiet the mind; it is in fact reaching the stillness that is already there, hidden underneath a shroud of all our thoughts and worries.

Deepak Chopra says in his book *Perfect Health*,

> *Physical impurities in cells have their equivalents in the mind: fear, anger, grief, greed, compulsiveness, doubt as well as all other negative emotions... and they can be as damaging as any chemical toxin. The mind-body connection turns negative attitudes into chemical toxins – "the stress hormones" that have been linked to so many diseases and health problems including infertility.*[8]

Meditation allows us to bypass that internal dialogue – that racing brain that is controlling us – and instead helps us to reach that place of inner peace and calm and tranquillity. This is the heart of the healing process.[9]

Mindfulness

> *Yesterday is gone. Tomorrow has not yet come. We have only today. Let us begin.*
>
> Mother Teresa

> *Yesterday has gone and with it has gone all the influences that could have made it different. Tomorrow is a myth or a mystery that we can colour with our own imagination, but today, this very moment is a gift, this moment is real and it is for this moment that we live, because soon that too will be gone, either seized upon and enjoyed or wasted.*[10]

Mindfulness, as the quotes above describe, is focusing on the here and now. So often we worry about things that have happened in the past and wish that we could have changed them – we worry about things that we should or should not have said. We often feel guilty about past experiences but if we keep digging up painful memories we are only re-infecting ourselves. Likewise we might worry about the future, and about things that we think may happen. But most of the things that we worry about won't happen anyway. So focusing on the here and now is a way of controlling than inner voice. Being mindful means being aware of the present moment and really noticing everything around you. You can be mindful at any time, in any place, while doing anything at all, from being in work to preparing a meal at home or going for a walk in the country.

Being mindful in work means that you completely focus on the task that you are doing, whether you are answering emails or writing a report or really paying attention if you are in a board meeting. Do not let your mind wander at all; become completely focused on the task you are doing without daydreaming or surfing the net! You can be mindful when you are in the shower, and instead of taking it for granted really focus on the warmth of the water washing over you, the smell of the soap and the shampoo and the suds in your hands as you wash your hair.

Be mindful in the kitchen when you prepare a meal. Notice the smell of the joint cooking, or the fresh salad as you slice the cucumber. When you are about to eat something, first of all take a close look at what you are about to eat and then make sure you eat mindfully by really savouring every mouthful and experiencing the different flavours and textures. Chew your food slowly, mindfully tasting every mouthful. So often we eat mindlessly, either reading or watching television while we munch away, not really noticing what we are eating.

When we walk mindfully we enhance the experience and joy of walking. Before you start, stand still outside for a moment to allow your thoughts to move to the here and now and take a few deep breaths in, savouring the fresh air. Try to walk in the country or through a park if you can, or along a riverbank. Experience the sun on your face or the wind in your hair, really listen to the birds singing or the hum of a bee or the slow drone of someone cutting the grass. Observe and notice everything around you from the different species of trees to the wildflowers and wildlife in the hedges. Notice the droplets of dew on the grass or the silky gossamer of a spider's web. Try not to think of anything at all, just keep focusing on your surroundings, but if your thoughts do distract you simply notice them and continue to focus on your breathing. There is something magical about being surrounded by the wonders of nature so just experience the sheer joy and pleasure of being outdoors and switch off your mind for a while and relax.

Being mindful is important if you are experiencing fertility problems because it brings you back to the here and now and helps stops the worry and the frustration. It is so easy to look back and think *I wish I hadn't been on the pill for so long*, or *I wish I hadn't left it so long before trying for a baby. I wish I hadn't had that miscarriage. Why was my last period so early?* It's so easy to allow your thoughts to become all consuming. Worrying about your next cycle – will you or won't you ovulate? Will it happen next month? When should you go and see about having IUI or IVF? What if nothing works? Mindfulness puts a STOP to the over active brain. Most of the things we worry about will never happen. Stop! Slow down and pull yourself back to the present time – make a list, mindfully, of all the good things in your life. This can help you to appreciate the good things you have, along with simple pleasures, and stops you focusing on the things you don't have. Focusing on the small pleasures in life can also mean that you really appreciate your family and friends and the love and friendships that surround you, helping you to get through this time in your life. Being mindful can help you focus on the positives in your life because when we are positive we produce hormones that make us feel good, reducing stress.

Vitamin D: The Sunshine Vitamin

Working long hours with not enough time for a lunch break, together with high sun protection factor (SPF) in our skin care, means that more and more women are becoming deficient in that all-important sunshine vitamin – vitamin D. Vitamin D is essential for strong and healthy bones, and for a healthy immune system. A deficiency of vitamin D has been linked to both miscarriage and an increased risk of pre-eclampsia in pregnancy. Research has found that in women with anovulatory dysfunction a staggering 93% were deficient in vitamin D. Vitamin D deficiency has also been linked to polycystic ovary syndrome and some autoimmune disorders such as multiple sclerosis and rheumatoid arthritis. It is though that supplementing with vitamin D may also improve the immune function of the placenta. The sun is not our only source of vitamin D as we can also get it from oily fish, eggs and milk, and some breakfast cereals and bread are fortified with it. Simple activities such as walking or cycling to work, walking to the shops or just taking a short walk during your lunch break should be enough to boost your vitamin D. However too much exposure to strong sunlight can be damaging to the skin, so be sensible and if you are going to be outside for long periods of time then do use sensible sun protection.

Awe Therapy

We've all been there – we've seen a spectacular view and the sight has filled us with awe. Well now there is research to show that when people experience the emotion of awe – such as seeing a beautiful view or witnessing a wonder of nature – they felt better about themselves and about life. The research from Stanford University in 2012 showed that just being outside in our beautiful countryside increased our physical and mental wellbeing. Awe therapy will mean different things to different people – a breath-taking view; a beautiful sunrise or sunset over the sea; walking through a bluebell wood or walking along a coast path with the wind or sea spray in your face. Whatever your interests get out into the fresh air and into our beautiful outdoors, experience the awe and feel the benefits.

Diet and Nutrition

Research shows that following a 'fertility diet' pattern may influence fertility in otherwise healthy women. Furthermore the majority of infertility cases due to ovulation disorders may be preventable through modifications of diet and lifestyle.[11]

Although this book is primarily about the emotions that hijack our fertility, I think it is worth mentioning something about diet and nutrition, because all too often when we are feeling low or a bit stressed we turn to food to make us feel better. We've all been there and the problem is that when we are stressed or worried we tend to reach for the junk food that's full of fats, bad carbohydrates and sugar! We quite often believe that we can eat our way out of a stressful situation, but the reality is we just feel worse – often guilty and lethargic, not to mention feeling bloated.

The food that we eat provides us with fuel that is converted into energy for use by our body. This energy is needed to support all the functions of the body. Diet is closely linked to emotions and the food that we eat can literally affect how we feel. This is because the nutrients in food act as neurochemicals. A diet high in protein can give a feeling of more energy, while a diet full of carbohydrates can make you feel sluggish, lethargic, hungry and depressed.[12]

What you eat can affect your emotions and the way you think and feel. Fluctuating blood sugar levels and deficiencies in some nutrients and amino acids can make you feel less motivated, depressed and lacking in energy. Avoiding excess sugar and processed foods can help to stabilise your blood sugar levels, making you feel better.

Taking a supplement of B vitamins and folic acid, which is essential in pregnancy to avoid neural defects such as spina bifida, can also help with the way we feel. Eating oily fish such as salmon or mackerel or taking a good omega 3 supplement is as important for our mood as it is for fertility. People who are deficient in omega 3 are more susceptible to depression. Omega 3 is also vital in pregnancy as it is important in the development of the foetal brain. New mums may be more prone to postnatal depression if they don't replace the omega 3 used by their baby during pregnancy.[13]

Research has shown that including omega 3 fatty acids in the diet has been shown to moderate the symptoms of autoimmune diseases such as endometriosis, as well as reducing natural killer cell activity and improving blood flow.[14] Further research also showed that women who were undergoing IVF and had higher levels of omega 3 in their system also produced better quality embryos.

It is now widely recognised that the most nutritious and healthy diet is the Mediterranean diet, and many fertility clinics are recommending that their patients follow this way of eating, because research showed that there was a 40% increased chance of treatment success in those women who followed a Mediterranean diet: whole grains such as oats, wholemeal bread and whole wheat pasta, brown rice and lots of colourful fruits and vegetables – at least five to seven a day and organic if possible

– with lean meat, and plenty of oily fish, and nuts and seeds. A Mediterranean diet may increase fertility because it is rich in vitamin B6 and folate.

All fruit and vegetables contain flavonoids, which are powerful antioxidants that can reverse the damage caused by free radicals. Flavonoids have also been shown to slow ageing and improve reproductive health overall. They appear to decrease blood clotting and enhance the action of vitamin C in building healthy blood vessel walls – all good news for fertility.[15]

Various foods have been shown to have properties such as decreasing inflammation or improving blood flow. Fresh ginger and spinach have been shown to reduce inflammation, while ginger also helps prevent blood clotting. Tomatoes help balance immune function while avocados help reduce inflammation. Citrus fruits have an anti-inflammatory action and rhubarb appears to improve blood flow. Onions and garlic contain selenium, which again regulates the immune system and contain blood-thinning compounds.

Other foods rich in antioxidants include broccoli, blueberries, prunes, blackberries and pomegranates. These are just a few examples and if you are concerned about your diet then please do see a nutritional therapist for further advice specific to your needs.

Generally speaking the Mediterranean, diet is a healthy and nutritious diet and in her book *The Impatient Woman's Guide to Getting Pregnant* Jean Twenge suggests the SOS diet, which is an easy way to remember the Mediterranean diet:

- S represents spinach, all fruit and vegetables and all healthy things
- O represents olives and olive oil, nuts and seeds, beans and legumes, and whole grains
- S represents salmon, oily fish and fish in general, and you could also include lean meat and protein here.[16]

Sugar is an absolute no-no because it is so bad for you! It tastes good because it is so sweet, but an injection of sugar in the bloodstream stimulates the same pleasure centre in the brain that responds to heroin and cocaine! That is one of the reasons why it is so addictive and why manufacturers add it to almost everything! Being aware of the dangers of too much sugar means that you can avoid it and make different choices. Sugar (sucrose) is made up of glucose and fructose. Glucose is metabolised by the cells throughout the body, but fructose is broken down by the liver. Fructose is the sugar that is added to soft drinks and confectionery, and if you eat too much of it too quickly the liver breaks down the fructose and produces fats called triglycerides. Some of the triglycerides are pushed out into the bloodstream and this results in increased blood pressure and the tissues becoming more resistant to insulin. The pancreas tries to control things by producing more insulin, but eventually metabolic syndrome occurs – fat deposits around the waist, high blood pressure, hormonal changes and a resistance to insulin.[17] PCOS is classed as a metabolic syndrome and can contribute to infertility. So cut down on refined sugar and try to avoid all convenience foods as they too will be high in sugar. Concentrate on fresh fruit and vegetables, oily fish and lean meat and whole grains.

How You Eat!

How you eat is also important because when we eat mindfully – slowly and savouring every mouthful, and every texture and taste – we eat less. When we are really aware of what we are eating we are less inclined to eat just for the sake of it. Try not to eat while reading or watching television if you can avoid it. And don't eat on the hoof while in work – always sit down away from your desk, or car if you travel a lot, and have a proper lunch break. You will enjoy and appreciate your food more and will be able to digest it better.

When we are tired or stressed we often reach for stimulants such as coffee to pick us up, or alcohol to help us relax! Neither is recommended if you are trying to conceive. Coffee in excess has been linked to miscarriage, but the occasional one won't harm you. Alcohol, should be avoided while trying to conceive but an occasional small glass of wine here or there may be just what the doctor ordered! Alcohol should however be avoided in pregnancy as recent research showed that in pregnant mums who had drank just one small glass of wine, foetal movements decreased for up to three hours afterwards.

Many of my patients become stressed over what and what not to eat, but keep it simple – lots of fruit and vegetables, lean meat and fish, a handful of nuts and seeds (provided you are not allergic to nuts of course!) and whole grains. Keep it simple – don't stress or beat yourself up over it if you go awry; just try to eat well 85% of the time.

Laugh and Have Fun

A day without laughter is a day wasted.

Charlie Chaplin

Laughter really is the best medicine! We all love a really good laugh! Can you remember the last time you laughed so much that tears ran down your face? And didn't you feel good for ages afterwards? The chances are, every time you remember that incident you continue to laugh or at least have a chuckle! Laughter is a wonderful way of expressing how happy we are feeling, but the neurochemistry of why we laugh is difficult to explain. When someone tells us a really good joke we laugh because the punch line is always unusual – it's not what we were expecting and we laugh because the ending surprises us. Research shows that laughter may come from the left prefrontal cortex, while worry and anxiety and other negative emotions come from the right side of the brain, therefore we cannot be happy and sad at the same time.

> *It is impossible for you to be angry and laugh at the same time.*
> *Anger and laughter are mutually exclusive and you have the*
> *power to choose either.*
>
> Wayne Dyer

Laughter has been used as a form of healing for many years and is a natural form of medicine. There are many advantages to laughter and these include boosting our physical, emotional and social health. Laughter therapy is beneficial and can enhance our life whatever our circumstances are.

The physical benefits of laughter include relieving anxiety and stress and reducing muscular tension. It boosts the immune system because it reduces the stress hormones, cortisol and adrenaline. When we laugh the brain also produces endorphins and these increase our feelings of wellbeing and can reduce pain. Laughter is thought to increase our antibody-producing cells, and it increases the function of T-cells – all resulting in a more efficient immune system. Laughter also improves circulation because when we laugh we take in more oxygen, improving the function of blood cells and vessels and increasing blood flow. The mental health benefits of laughing include decreasing anxiety and fear, decreasing stress, and improving our mood and zest for life.

Laughter makes you feel good and that feeling stays with you long after the laughter has subsided. Laughter helps us remain positive and optimistic through difficult situations and loss. Laughter helps give us the courage and strength to find a new meaning and hope. Even in the most difficult of situations a laugh or a smile can really make you feel better. When you laugh you experience the world from a completely different point of view, making you feel more relaxed and more positive, happier and able to put everything into perspective. Lighten up and stop taking yourself too seriously. Look back at embarrassing moments, bring humour into your conversations and laugh at situations instead of moaning about them. Spend time with people who make you laugh, be more spontaneous and try to find humour in every aspect of your life. Surround yourself with things that help you to lighten up – a funny poster, photos of people laughing, or a funny screen saver. Do some fun activities such as going bowling with a group of friends, or playing mini golf – it always has me in fits of laughter. Watch comical TV programmes or funny films – life can be fun! Keep things in perspective – many things in life are beyond our control. Put the fun back into fertility.

There have been studies showing that laughter can improve the outcome of IVF, and a study in Israel showed that women who were entertained by a clown immediately after their embryo transfer had a 36.4% success rate while the women not seen by the clown only had a 20.2% chance of success. It is thought that the humour created by observing the clown had a relaxing effect on the women who were stressed out by years of fertility treatment.

A smile is the beginning of laughter. Smile at yourself in the mirror, smile at people in work, smile at people in the street and smile at the cashier in the supermarket – you'll make their day and when they smile back at you, you'll feel as though you've received a gift.

A smile costs nothing, but gives so much. It enriches those who receive without making poorer those who give. It takes but a moment, but the memory of it sometimes lasts forever. None is so rich or mighty that he can get along without it, and none is so poor but that he can be made rich by it. A smile creates happiness in the home, fosters goodwill in business, and is the countersign of friendship. It brings rest to the weary, cheer to the discouraged, sunshine to the sad, and it is nature's best antidote for trouble. Yet it cannot be bought, begged, borrowed or stolen, for it is something that is of no value to anyone until it is given away. Some people are too tired to give you a smile; give them one of yours, as none needs a smile so much as he who has no more to give.

Anon

Visualisation

What the mind of man can conceive and believe, it can achieve.
Napoleon Hill

The most remarkable feature of imagery work is that it can be accompanied by physiological changes.
Gerald Epstein MD, *Healing Visualisations*

Visualisation has been used for many years to help people achieve success. Professional sportspeople and athletes have always been encouraged to visualise their success. A study in America divided a basketball team into three groups. The first group were asked to practise shooting at goal for 20 minutes every day. The second group were told to visualise shooting at goal, while the third group were told to do nothing. At the end of the two weeks the groups were assessed by seeing how many goals they could score. The visualisation group were able to score almost as many goals as the group who practised. Every time they visualised scoring they were increasing the feeling and the memory of how to be successful; they were increasing new pathways in the brain – neurogenesis.

Visualisation is incredibly powerful and can equally work against you as it can for you. The mind is a very powerful part of the body and both failure and success are figments of our imagination. The brain has difficulty in determining what's true and what's imagined. We've all experienced the worry when our partner or another member of our family have been late home from work – we imagine that they have been involved in an accident and can almost visualise the car upside down in a hedge. The ensuing stress response is tangible – our heart races and we have a sick feeling in our stomach as we enter fight-or-flight mode. The relief when they arrive home is then converted into anger – 'Why didn't you ring to say you'd be late? I've been worried sick.' Our imagination convinced the brain that our partner *had* been in an accident and our body responded accordingly. Likewise when we visualise a positive event we experience feelings of joy and excitement, and the brain then produces hormones such as endorphins and serotonin that make us feel good. So by visualising we are fooling the unconscious brain into believing that we've already achieved something before it actually happens. Visualisation can be really important in helping us to achieve our goal in life.

When we are immersed in negative thoughts and beliefs it is important to try and break this pattern and one of the best ways is by visualisation. The more you visualise the new picture, the stronger it will become. Visualisation is a wonderful way of rewiring the brain and redirecting your internal thoughts to challenge your negative beliefs. In negative thinking – *I'll never become pregnant*, or *I'll never be a mum* – the same thoughts and beliefs have been established and it is easier for the brain to continue with that belief/ thought than it is to think or see a new one and to form new pathways in the brain. But the more you visualise the positive outcome, the stronger those new connections will become and new pathways will be formed.

To achieve the best results with visualisation you must believe it can happen and you must generate the same feelings and emotions that would feel if you had already achieved your dreams. Seeing the image is not enough – you have to really *feel* your dream; show your brain what feelings it has to look out for – the joy and happiness of being pregnant, of engaging with and feeling that love for your baby. Feel the excitement as you look at the positive pregnancy test, as you tell your family and friends you are pregnant. Visualisation is a simple and successful way of speeding up the process and fooling the unconscious brain into achieving something before you have.

> *I'm convinced I became pregnant because I was able to see a very clear picture of myself holding my newborn baby in my arms. Although I found it extremely painful at first, the more I visualised the easier it became until every time I visualised my baby I became so excited at the prospect of being a mum – and then it happened! I can't thank you enough.*

So many of my patients find it very difficult to visualise being pregnant or even see themselves with a baby. They are too frightened and too scared to visualise themselves with something they want so badly in case it never happens. And so the thing they want most of all in the world is being pushed further away into the back of the mind. This however can send mixed messages to the brain – do you or don't you want a baby?

Visualisation can be used with fertility in so many ways:

- Visualise the different stages in the menstrual cycle – the follicle growing and developing, being released by the ovary; the fronds of the fallopian tube wafting it towards a sperm
- Visualise a healthy womb with a beautifully thick and spongy lining ready to envelop an implanting embryo

- Visualise the embryo nestling down into the warm folds of the uterus
- Visualise that embryo developing into a beautiful baby
- You may wish to visualise your womb after surgery, seeing how healthy it now looks after any endometriosis has been removed
- Some women visualise reducing their high FSH levels
- Some women visualise reducing their levels of NK cells
- You may wish to visualise your womb as a secure and protective home over the next nine months for your baby
- You may just wish to see yourself pregnant, with a bump growing bigger and bigger every month
- Or you may wish to focus on the birth itself, seeing yourself breathing easily through each contraction as your body prepares for the delivery of your baby

When I asked one of my patients who had had several miscarriages in the past what sprung to mind when she thought about her womb, her first reaction was that it looked like a broken and cracked vase, unable to hold water and all the flowers in it had died. With guidance she was able to correct this image by taking the vase apart in her mind and gluing each piece securely together so that there were no cracks visible at all. She was then able to visualise filling it with water and seeing beautiful flower buds open up. She practised this visualisation every day for several weeks, and went on to have a beautiful baby girl.

Make your visualisation vivid and keep practising every day for 10–20 minutes. It will get easier the more you practise and your visualisations will become more vivid and more real. To get the most out of visualisation try to start with a period of relaxation or deep breathing as it is easier to visualise when we are relaxed. If we are in a state of high arousal, i.e. anxious or stressed, it is harder to imagine things. When you visualise a future event for yourself such as seeing yourself pregnant or holding your baby, you are increasing the power of expectation and by creating a positive expectation for yourself you are actually strengthening the chances of a positive outcome.

Visualisation is a wonderful way of empowering yourself and is much more positive than worrying about a negative outcome. I encourage my IVF patients to do this – to visualise a positive pregnancy test and imagine how they will feel when they see the blue line showing they are pregnant, instead of worrying about what happens when this cycle doesn't work again!

Affirmations

Though no-one can go back and make a brand new start, anyone can start from now and make a brand new ending.

Carl Bard

An affirmation, put simply, is a positive thought. It is a short positive thought or statement that means something to you, and that you want to be true. An affirmation is a self-help tool that can help you to reinforce and maintain change in your body. Repeating these healthy messages can become a part of your inner voice and can change your beliefs and rewire your brain. The more often you repeat these positive messages the greater the connections or pathways they make in your brain. Repeating a statement about something being true will create new pathways in the brain introducing a new sensory idea. This is particularly useful when your brain is used to receiving a stream of negative thoughts and beliefs.[18] In a way you are fooling your brain into believing that something is true. The more often you repeat them, the stronger those connections and beliefs become.

- Whatever happens, I can cope with it
- My body is healthy
- My womb is healthy and ready for a baby
- My ovaries work perfectly
- My tubes are free and clear
- I am ready now for a baby
- I will be a good mother
- I have belief in my body
- I am confident I will get pregnant
- I CAN do this!

In the same way as visualisation, affirmations work best when you are calm and relaxed and are in a quiet area where you can really focus on repeating the positive statements. Soon you will come to believe them and will look forward to your time or your window for affirmations each day, and you will become excited by the positive feelings they create in you. You will soon regain faith and confidence in yourself and your body and these feelings will grow more and more each day as you continue to repeat these positive beliefs.

Gratitude

Gratitude is the healthiest of all human emotions. The more you express gratitude for what you have, the more likely you will have even more to express gratitude for.

Zig Ziglar

Gratitude makes sense of our past, brings peace for today, and creates a vision for tomorrow.

Melody Beattie

So often we complain about the things we don't have, and we are all guilty of it from time to time! When we have a power cut or our water supply is disrupted we all complain about the electricity that's not there or the water that's been cut off! But we never appreciate them when they are working perfectly. The good thing about gratitude is that you focus on what you have; we focus on others and by being grateful we count our blessings. When we are grateful we are not focusing on 'me' but on other things and other people, and it stops the 'woe is me' attitude.

By being grateful and saying 'thank you', we are training our mind to think positively, and being grateful can also be incredibly healing. It helps us to put everything into perspective and to appreciate everything we do have. It has a very positive effect on our body by releasing endorphins and increasing our feeling of wellbeing. Try to start every day before you get out of bed by making a list of everything you are grateful for:

- Thank you for the warmth and comfort of my bed
- Thank you for my beautiful house
- Thank you for the cup of tea brought to me by my partner
- Thank you for all the people supporting me through this difficult time
- Thank you for the medical staff helping me through this IVF cycle
- Thank you for a beautiful day – the sun is shining and the birds are singing
- Thank you for my beautiful garden – for the shrubs and flowers
- Thank you for waking me up and for my healthy body
- Thank you for the beautiful countryside – the fields and trees; the rivers and streams
- Thank you for all my family and friends, and everyone I love and who loves me
- Thank you, thank you, thank you... the list is endless!

Make a list that's relevant to you. Try to keep the list with you all the time and then if things don't always go your way or if you feel a bit down or disappointed in any way just remind yourself of all the good things you have in your life and it will help to make you feel better about yourself and put everything into perspective.

We should be appreciating these things every day while we have them. Be thankful for everything you have in your life and focus on all the good things; don't just focus on the things you haven't got.

Forgiveness

Research has shown that the act of forgiveness can reduce anxiety and depression as well as improving our feelings of hope and self-esteem. Everyone has an incident in their lives that they wish they could change, or wish hadn't happened or had worked out differently, but learning to forgive and move on and not dwell on it can really improve your outcome. You can feel stronger and more empowered by learning to forgive, and it will also improve your physical and mental health. Learning to forgive and move on can give you a feeling of inner peace and relief.

Holding onto feelings of anger, revenge and bitterness only makes us miserable and actually affects our health and wellbeing. Letting go of negative emotions has been shown to have a positive effect on health by reducing stress, improving circulation and boosting the immune system, all of which are crucial to fertility.

You may find it difficult at first to 'forgive' your best friend, or sister, or work colleague for getting pregnant before you, but do try to forgive them and you will soon feel that you actually feel better and less stressed about it.

Music

Most of us enjoy music in some form or other. I play soft, relaxing music for my patients during their acupuncture or hypnotherapy treatment and it really does seem to have a relaxing effect. But not many of us realise how music can be really therapeutic, and research has shown that when relaxing music was played to doctors at a conference, their pulse rates decreased, and likewise when a faster, more upbeat piece of music was played their pulse rates increased accordingly. Their bodies were being manipulated by the music, as it were. Ayurveda medicine recognises that music can be used to balance the body and the mind. When we listen to music or take part in singing in a choir or singing carols at Christmas time it gives us pleasure, and we know that pleasure can change the physiology of the body. When we feel good we produce endorphins – the feel-good hormones. Music can be soothing and calming. Research has shown that listening to soft, slow classical music can lower blood pressure.[19] Equally, listening to uplifting music can boost the mood, as was found by researchers at the University of Missouri in the US. So whatever your mood, put on some music – if you feel stressed put on some gentle, relaxing music and if you feel down in the dumps raise the beat and dance around the room. Feel that tension ebbing away as you tune in to the effects that music has on your physiology.

Belief and Trust (and Age)

If you think you can or you think you can't, either way you are right.

Henry Ford

First of all we have to have belief – belief in ourselves, belief in the health professionals who are looking after us and belief in our bodies. After all, the body is designed to heal itself. We know this because if we get a blister on our foot or we burn ourselves on the oven, in a few days' time these injuries will have healed up. We were all born with a miraculous inbuilt healing capacity that is designed to heal just about any problem we have, and this healing system is our immune system. A healthy immune system can heal just about anything, provided the immune system itself is functioning properly.

The one thing that turns the immune system off is physiological stress on the body. So if stress affects our immune system and our immune system heals just about everything, then it follows that stress must be the root cause of all disease. Get rid of stress and the immune system functions normally again, and hey presto, the body is healed![20]

The Placebo Effect

The power of belief is called the placebo effect in medicine. According to a study published in the *New York Times* in 2008, half of all doctors in the USA prescribe placebos! Why? Because placebos work![21]

Twenty years ago I was diagnosed with grade three aggressive breast cancer which had also spread to my lymph nodes. I went to the hospital to get my results with my husband and our four children aged six and under (it didn't occur to me that the news would not be good). When I received the diagnosis I was completely distraught, but then my consultant said the best thing he could have said to me: '*Yes, there are problems and I won't pretend that there aren't, but there is nothing that we can't overcome and you will see your grandchildren.*' I am convinced that my trust and belief in Mr Webster (hearing him imply that not only would I see my children grow up, but also see my grandchildren), and my belief in myself and that I had far too much to do in the future, contributed to the fact that I am still here today!

If you talk to any oncologist they will suggest that the patients with a positive approach to their condition often appear to do better than those patients that have a more negative approach to treatment. The patients who believe they will get well again quite often have a more positive outcome. Can the same be said for those patients going through fertility treatment? When my patients first come to see me they are too afraid to believe that one day they will have a baby, one way or another. This is something that they want so much that they are too afraid to believe it could happen in case it doesn't! Many women going through IVF are too afraid or anxious to believe that the cycle could work. They obviously really, really want it to work but they hold themselves back 'just in case'. You can't give your brain mixed messages.

Our beliefs cause actual physical effects throughout the body. If we remember the story about the caveman earlier in the book, we produce serotonin and endorphins – our feel-good hormones – when we think and act in positive ways. When we feel good we don't activate the stress response; instead we feel calm and relaxed, but when we think negative thoughts we go into fight-or-flight mode. Our thoughts manifest into our feelings and our feelings into physical effects in the body. If a woman is trying to get pregnant but is immersed in negative thoughts most of the time, what message is that sending to her body? Our cells are listening!

Health is the most precious thing in life, and yet more than anything else we take our health for granted. For many of us, the only time we think of our health is when we lose it. Then realisation hits us: without our health we have nothing. Rhonda Byrne, The Magic p.51

The Nocebo Effect

This is the opposite of the placebo effect. Just like the placebo effect, wherein the body will attempt to follow positive suggestions given to it by the mind, the nocebo effect is where negative suggestions are thought, believed and followed. I believe an example of this is when women approaching their early 30s are worried about their fertility. There is so much in the media about women leaving it too late to start a family, and how their body clock is ticking away. I think women stress about this far more than is talked about, and the belief that they will struggle to conceive becomes very much a reality. The ensuing stress brought about then creates further problems and it becomes a vicious circle. Dr Elizabeth Muir, an eminent clinical psychologist in London who specialises in fertility and childbirth, says that *In regard to women and the time left on the biological clock, I believe that psychological and emotional factors, not age, have much more influence on a woman's chance of conceiving.*

According to Jean Twenge in her book *The Impatient Woman's Guide to Getting Pregnant*, statistics on age and childbearing are taken from records from 17th-century France! More recent studies showed that 85% of 35–39 year olds became pregnant after one year of regular unprotected intercourse!

Another example of the nocebo effect is where a woman is told that her FSH (follicle stimulating hormone) levels are so high that she has premature ovarian failure and is in early menopause, and will not be able to have children unless she has IVF with donor eggs. Also, because the message is delivered by a person in great authority – a medical consultant – her belief that she will never conceive naturally becomes paramount. FSH is measured by a blood test on days one to three of the menstrual cycle. A reading below ten generally means that the ovaries are producing follicles. A reading greater than ten, however, suggests that the ovaries may not be functioning as well and may not be producing many follicles. FSH is strongly affected by stress and so a woman who is highly stressed – and even more so having been given the diagnosis of premature ovarian failure – may not get an accurate reading based on her FSH levels alone. This has been the case in many of my patients, but with the help of acupuncture and relaxation techniques, they have gone on to conceive naturally and have subsequent pregnancies.

The nocebo effect is extremely powerful and affects women trying to conceive in many ways, including those who have had surgery for endometriosis and who have been told to try to conceive quickly because they only have a small window before the endometriosis returns! It also affects those who have had previous miscarriages or IVF failure. Women often believe the same thing will happen again. Positive thinking, affirmations and visualisation are what is needed here to help these women regain confidence in themselves and their bodies, as well as relaxation or meditation, or similar mind-body techniques.

References

1. Geshe Kelsang Gyatso, *Eight Steps to Happiness*, Tharpa Publications, UK, 2012
2. Help Guide. How much sleep do you need? http://www.helpguide.org/articles/sleep/how-much-sleep-do-you-need.htm (accessed 14th June 2014)
3. Wikipedia. Physical Exercise. https://en.wikipedia.org/wiki/Physical_exercise (accessed 17th /june 2014)
4. John J. Ratey and Eric Hagerman, *Spark! How Exercise Will Improve the Performance of Your Brain*, Quercus, London, 2010, p60
5. John J. Ratey and Eric Hagerman, *Spark! How Exercise Will Improve the Performance of Your Brain*, Quercus, London, 2010
6. Elizabeth Palermo. What is Qigong? http://www.livescience.com/38192-qigong.html (accessed 20th June 2014)
7. Herbert Benson, MD, *Timeless Healing*, Simon and Schuster, New York, 1997, p139
8. Deepak Chopra MD, *Perfect Health*, Bantam Books, London, 2001, p157
9. Deepak Chopra MD, *Perfect Health*, Bantam Books, London, 2001
10. Adapted from *Game Players Planet* by kind permission from David Newton, the Clifton Practice, Bristol, http://www.cpht.co.uk
11. *Obstetrics and Gynaecology* 2007 Nov; 110(5):1050–8
12. Shawn Talbott, *The Cortisol Connection*, Hunter House, Alameda, 2007
13. Joe Griffin and Ivan Tyrrell, *How to Lift Depression Fast*, HG Publishing, Great Britain, 2009
14. Alan E. Beer, MD, *Is Your Body Baby Friendly?* AJR Publishing, USA, 2006
15. *Ibid*
16. Jean M. Twenge, *The Impatient Woman's Guide to Getting Pregnant*, ATRIA Paperback, New York, 2012
17. Richard Cohen, *Bottom of the Drink*, National Geographic, August 2013, 82–97
18. Herbert Benson, MD, *Timeless Healing*, Simon and Schuster, New York, 1997
19. Deepak Chopra MD, *Perfect Health*, Bantam Books, London, 2001

20. Alexander Loyd, PhD and Ben Johnson MD, *The Healing Code*, Hodder and Stoughton, London, 2011

21. *Ibid*

Chapter Seven

Complementary Therapies

Maybe you have tried all the self-help techniques in the previous chapters, but perhaps you want to do more. Maybe you feel better working alongside a practitioner, or you have read positive things about acupuncture and IVF. Perhaps you have used acupuncture in the past and it helped you, or maybe you enjoy the 'me time' you get from going to see a therapist. Whatever your reason for doing complementary therapies, feel empowered by taking that decision, relax and enjoy them.

Complementary therapies are holistic forms of treatment that can complement other forms of medicine or treatment. Complementary therapies may not have all the answers, but they can contribute a huge amount because they look at the bigger picture. They will look at and assess you holistically. They will look at you as a whole and consider everything about you – your general health, your personality, your lifestyle, your job, your emotional health, your family health and your diet.

Sadly when it comes to unexplained infertility, allopathic or conventional medicine will test your hormone levels to make sure you are ovulating, check that your fallopian tubes are clear and test your partner's sperm. What they don't do however is look at you as a whole. So many of my patients with so-called unexplained infertility have other symptoms such as IBS, migraine or poor sleeping patterns, and their nails may be bitten down to the quick! All symptoms of emotional stress.

Each system of complementary therapy is unique and each has its own strengths. Success with these forms of treatment lies in choosing one that feels right for you, that you are comfortable with and that is appropriate for your problem. Sadly most women only turn to complementary therapies as a last resort, particularly when it comes to fertility. They will have tried everything there is to try – Clomid, IUI and IVF – and often it is only then when all else has failed that they will turn to complementary therapies to help them as they try yet another round of IVF. In reality these therapies could have helped them on their journey, complementing every procedure and reducing their stress and anxiety as well as creating some physiological changes along the way. Acupuncture in particular improves blood flow to the uterus and ovaries and reduces levels of the stress hormone cortisol. What most people don't realise is that there is increasing evidence to support the use of complementary therapies in infertility, and acupuncture and hypnotherapy are two areas where much research has been done.

Women also have different expectations from complementary therapies – some will want to reduce stress, others will want to alleviate some symptoms such as painful periods or the pain of endometriosis, some will want to increase their feeling of wellbeing and feel that they are doing something to help, whereas others will be looking for a complete cure!

There are very many different forms of complementary therapies, but the two I'm going to focus on for the purpose of this book are acupuncture and hypnotherapy. Both have been proven to reduce stress and to promote the relaxation response, and have evidence to support their use in fertility. I will, however, also briefly mention reflexology, abdominal massage, Reiki and aromatherapy.

Acupuncture is one of the oldest forms of medicine and originated in China over three thousand years ago. It is also the most researched form of complementary therapy and thousands of studies have been carried out worldwide showing it to be effective for a wide range of health problems. Acupuncture is now accepted all over the world as a valid system of health care and more and more medical doctors are recognising its benefits. According to Traditional Chinese Medicine (TCM), of which acupuncture is a part, our health is dependent on the body's motivating energy (or *Qi*) moving in a smooth and balanced way through a series of channels (or meridians) throughout the body. When the *Qi* flows freely, the body is in a healthy state. If the *Qi* becomes unbalanced or stuck, then disharmony and illness may result. Emotional disturbances such as anxiety, anger, grief, overwork, stress or even a poor diet may affect the flow of *Qi* in the body. The stimulation of appropriate acupuncture points with very fine sterile needles will regulate the flow of energy and restore health and wellbeing. The aim is to stimulate the body's own healing response and regain natural balance.

From a Western point of view, inserting acupuncture needles into the body stimulates the production of beta-endorphins. This increases the feeling of wellbeing, helping the patient to feel good, and also encourages the body's own internal healing mechanisms. There is evidence to show that acupuncture reduces sympathetic tone, which is the sympathetic nervous system − in other words our fight-or-flight − and as a result decreases our stress response. Reducing stress has been shown to help with hormonal balance, as well as improving blood flow to the pelvic organs, which in theory could increase the chances of conceiving.

Over the last decade or so the use of acupuncture in fertility medicine has grown and more women are now turning to it as an adjunct to accompany fertility treatment such as IVF, as well as using it as a standalone treatment for unexplained infertility.

The first study to look at acupuncture and IVF was carried out in 2002 when a German doctor named Paulus looked at 160 women undergoing IVF. Half had acupuncture immediately before and after embryo transfer, while the other group of 80 rested for the same time immediately before and after embryo transfer. The results were interesting – the acupuncture group had a 42% success rate compared with 26% in the non-acupuncture group. It is thought that the acupuncture increased blood flow to the womb and relaxed the muscles, improving the chances of implantation. Further studies have been carried out over the years and in 2008 a systematic review and meta-analysis in the *British Medical Journal*, followed by a further systematic review and meta-analysis in *Fertility and Sterility* in 2012, concluded that acupuncture can improve the clinical pregnancy rate (CPR) and live birth rate (LBR) among women undergoing IVF. The *British Medical Journal* concluded that women who had acupuncture alongside their IVF were 65% more likely to have a successful embryo transfer, and of those a staggering 91% went on to have a live birth.

Further research by Elizabet Stener-Victorin in Sweden also found that acupuncture may help to:

- Improve blood flow to the uterus and ovaries
- Increase the chances of ovulation in women with PCOS
- Reduce the stress hormones that prevent ovulation
- Improve the chance of success in women going through IVF

Using acupuncture to assist with fertility issues, and indeed to accompany IVF, is a complex process and so it is essential that you choose a practitioner who is experienced in this field of medicine. Don't be afraid to ask them how many women like yourself they have seen in the past.

Hypnotherapy

Hypnosis is a peaceful, creative and productive state of inner absorption. It is a natural learning state that occurs from within. Hypnosis is a natural human ability and a powerful tool for change.

Stephen Gilligan

Hypnotherapy is a form of mind-body medicine, and takes place when a person is in a state of deep relaxation, or a hypnotic trance. Hypnosis is where both conscious and subconscious minds come together. It is a state of being in a deep trance. We experience trance every day – it is a natural state that happens when we are completely focused on one thing, such as when we are immersed in a book or engrossed while watching a film and our attention becomes completely focused on that one thing. A similar relaxed state can also be achieved while doing meditation or visualisation – this is seen as self-hypnosis. When we enter a hypnotic trance we become deeply relaxed. The parasympathetic nervous system is activated, while our fight-or-flight or sympathetic nervous system is switched off. Physiological changes occur in the body – our breathing slows down, our heart rate decreases and our blood pressure drops. The levels of cortisol decrease and our body moves into a deeply relaxed state. Being in a deeply hypnotic state or trance is very similar to being in REM sleep, and this is where we have access to the subconscious mind.

Hypnotherapy can help replace negative thoughts and beliefs with positive thoughts, suggestions and images. It can help you to focus on the positive aspects of your life, to feel better about yourself, and focus on the things you can do as opposed to the things you can't do. It can increase feelings of wellbeing and relaxation and help you feel less stressed. Hypnosis can also help process negative emotions such as anger or fear. When we are in a state of high emotional arousal we lose the ability to be rational. Hypnotherapy helps reduce that arousal, allowing us to be calmer and to see things from a different perspective.

Hypnotherapy may help with fertility because it is thought to reduce levels of the hormone prolactin, which inhibits ovulation. Research also showed that hypnotherapy can double the chances of having a successful IVF outcome. It can change your perspective and help you to focus on the positive things you are doing instead of dwelling on the negative. Hypnotherapy may help by harnessing the power of your own mind to work with you, instead of against you. It can help you visualise a preferred future for yourself.

Research has shown that managing and reducing stress can help overcome fertility problems, whether you are trying naturally or undergoing assisted reproduction treatment. Complementary therapies such as acupuncture or hypnotherapy or both may help you achieve a relaxed state of mind and a positive outlook as well as feeling better about yourself as you journey towards motherhood.

Other Complementary Therapies

It is important to choose a therapy that suits you. If you do not like needles then rather than persevere with acupuncture, try acupressure instead. Most acupuncture practitioners will be pleased to show you a selection of acupressure points and it is something that you could do at home.

Reflexology, abdominal massage, Reiki and aromatherapy are all complementary therapies than can help you relax and feel better about yourself. There is little evidence to speak of to suggest that these may help with infertility, but the main thing is if you enjoy them and it's a little bit of 'me time' for you and helps you relax, then go for it.

Reflexology

Reflexology is a healing therapy based on the principle that all body systems are represented on the feet and hands in the form of specific reflex areas. A professionally trained reflexologist stimulates these reflex areas using gentle massage techniques. This may help to reduce blockages in energy pathways, encouraging the body to work naturally to restore its own healthy balance.

Many people use reflexology as a way of relaxing the mind and body, but the therapy can offer much more than this. A reflexologist cannot offer a cure, but the therapy has been shown to be effective in the treatment of hormonal imbalance, regulating the menstrual cycle and improving blood circulation.

Abdominal Massage

I often encourage my patients and/or their partners to perform some gentle abdominal massage in the lead-up to ovulation. So many women carry tension in their abdomen and massage is useful for releasing this tension, and also for encouraging blood flow. Sometimes the abdomen appears cold or cool to the touch and I often encourage the use of a heat pack or hot water bottle before massage. This should only be done in the days before ovulation – if in doubt, then don't use it.

Many women are now exploring the use of Maya abdominal massage, or uterine massage. The object of this massage is to ensure the uterus is in the correct place for conception. Maya abdominal massage is a non-invasive technique based on ancient Mayan healing.

Reiki

Reiki is an ancient form of healing which is used to achieve balance and harmony within the body. To achieve optimum health we need to have the physical, mental and emotional aspects of our life in harmony. Reiki healing is the channelling of energy through the hands of a qualified Reiki practitioner, and is thought to stimulate the natural healing processes of the body.

Reiki can be used safely as an adjunct to conventional medical advice and treatment as well as in combination with other complementary therapies. Some people find Reiki helps them to feel better by reducing stress and promoting relaxation. There is no evidence to support its use in fertility.

Aromatherapy

Aromatherapy is a healing therapy that uses the healing and therapeutic properties of essential oils during massage. The essential oils are absorbed into the body through the skin, inhaling through the nose and mouth and through bathing in them, when a few drops may be added to your bath water, making for a relaxing bath. It is thought that inhaled oils will stimulate the limbic system of the brain and may have a relaxing effect whilst also boosting mood.

It is important to see a trained practitioner as some oils are contraindicated in pregnancy or if think you might be pregnant.

Chapter Eight

Summing It All Up

For the really busy women who don't have the time to read the whole book – this chapter is for you! It sums it all up in a nutshell! This is a brief summary of all the self-help techniques that have been discussed, and to help you remember the basics I've come up with an acronym. This chapter sums it all up in an easy-to-remember format. This is my Fertility Programme for emotional health.

FERTILITY

- F is for food – fresh fruit and vegetables, fresh fish and a Mediterranean diet
- E is for exercise – moderate exercise and being outdoors
- R is for relaxation – including meditation
- T is for thoughts – think positive thoughts
- I is for imagination – imagine yourself being pregnant
- L is for laughter – laugh, lighten up and have fun
- I is for inner voice – stop that inner voice, the worrying, and practise mindfulness
- T is for thank you – say thank you and be grateful for what you already have
- Y is for YES – 'Yes, I will become a mum' – believe and trust in yourself and your body

F is for Food, Fresh Fruit and Vegetables, Fresh Fish and a
Mediterranean Diet

The food you eat can directly affect your emotions and the way you feel and think. Deficiencies in some nutrients and fluctuating blood sugar levels can make you feel depressed and lacking in energy.

Research has shown that women who followed a Mediterranean diet had a 40% increased chance of success with IVF.

Oily fish – salmon, mackerel, sardines or tuna, or taking a good omega 3 supplement – is as important for your mood as it is for fertility. The other benefits of oily fish/supplements are:

- It is important for the developing foetal brain
- It has been shown to moderate the symptoms of autoimmune diseases such as endometriosis
- May reduce natural killer cell activity
- Improves blood flow
- Research shows that women undergoing IVF with high levels of omega 3 had better quality embryos.

All fruit and vegetables contain flavonoids which have been shown to slow ageing and improve reproductive health overall. They have been shown to decrease blood clotting and improve circulation – great news for fertility.

Foods to eat for fertility:

- Fruit and vegetables – at least five to seven portions a day, and as many different colourful varieties as possible
- Fresh fish – oily fish, salmon, mackerel, sardines, pilchards, tuna. Include lean meat, chicken and eggs here too
- Whole grains – wholemeal bread, whole wheat pasta, brown rice, oats

- Nuts, seeds and olives. A good handful of unsalted nuts and seeds – Brazil nuts, almonds, walnuts, sunflower seeds and pumpkin seeds

A typical plate should be half vegetables or salad, one quarter protein and one quarter carbohydrates.

E is for Exercise – Moderate Exercise and Being Outdoors

Exercise can benefit fertility in so many ways because it improves all aspects of our health. Regular and moderate amounts of exercise can:

- Reduce stress by using up excess cortisol (stress hormone)
- Boost the immune system, preventing disease and inflammation in the body
- Improve the circulation and prevent blood clotting
- Regulate insulin, preventing metabolic syndrome (e.g. PCOS)
- Help with regeneration of brain cells and management of emotions (keeps us balanced), as well as improving memory
- Make us feel happier by boosting our feel-good hormones – endorphins

Make exercise as much a part of your life as eating and sleeping. If you choose an exercise that you enjoy it will become part of your life and your daily routine. Try walking or cycling to work, or at least part of the way, go swimming or have a game of tennis. Perhaps dancing or rock climbing is more to your taste. Whatever your sport just go out and do it – you'll be surprised how much better you feel.

One of the quickest ways to relax is to slow down your breathing. If you suddenly become anxious, angry, stressed or overwhelmed by something, just stop and slow your breathing down. Breathe in to a count of three and out to a count of six. Just doing this a few times will help you to feel better and in control again.

So many people these days don't seem to be able to stop and do nothing, even for ten minutes. We are so used to being stimulated from the outside that we find it difficult to relax without turning the television on or watching something on the laptop.

Relaxing and doing nothing is important for clearing our minds and for clearing out all the rubbish – all the negative thoughts, past and present that accumulate and make us feel stressed.

Don't feel guilty about relaxing for a few minutes every day. In the long run you will feel better, calmer and will be more constructive and able to cope in other areas of your life. Remember the research that suggested that those who practised regular meditation had a younger biological age and increased levels of DHEA compared to those who did not meditate.

T is for Thoughts – Think Positive Thoughts

Our body is a product of our thoughts. There is now evidence to show that the way we think really can affect our biology and our body.

When we think positive thoughts we feel calm, relaxed and more optimistic. When we think negative thoughts we become anxious and stressed because every negative thought is a bad thought. Our thoughts transform into physical effects in the body. We now know that our cells react and respond to everything we do, including the way we think. This results in a profound effect on our physiology, including our hormones, circulation and immune system – all of which can affect fertility.

If you are trying to get pregnant but are immersed in negative thoughts most of the time, what messages are you sending to your body? If you are constantly thinking about your fertility, worrying and feeling frustrated because you can't control it, then STOP!

Instead, turn your thoughts around and think about all the positive things you are doing to improve your health, lifestyle and fertility – healthy eating, moderate exercise and relaxation, as well as managing your thoughts. All of those will generate positive feelings which will translate into a positive effect on your physiology and will actually help your fertility.

I is for Imagination and Visualisation – Imagine Yourself Being Pregnant

> *Whatever the mind can achieve and believe, it can conceive.*
> Napoleon Hill

Imagination and visualisation have been used for years to help people attain success. Visualising and imagining something can actually increase new pathways in the brain – something called neurogenesis. When we really *imagine* a positive event or outcome we experience feelings of joy and excitement, and we produce hormones such as endorphins and serotonin that make us feel good.

By imagining our dream we can actually fool the subconscious brain into believing we've achieved something before it actually happens. To achieve the best results you must really believe it can happen and you must generate the same feelings and emotions that you would feel if you had already achieved your dream. Feel the excitement as you imagine looking at a positive pregnancy test, and imagine how happy you will feel as you tell your family and friends that you are pregnant.

Make your imagination really vivid and practise it every day for 10–20 minutes. It will get easier the more you do it.

Imagination and visualisation is a wonderful way of empowering yourself, and is much more positive than stressing about a negative outcome.

L is for Laughter – Laugh, Lighten Up and Have Fun

Laughter really is the best medicine and has been used as a form of healing for many years.

Laughter boosts our physical, emotional and social health. It boosts our circulation and relieves anxiety and stress. It boosts our immune system by reducing cortisol and adrenaline, increases our antibody-producing cells and the function of our T-cells. Laughter makes us feel good and that feeling will last long after the laughter has subsided.

There has been some research to show that laughter can actually improve the outcome of IVF. I always encourage my patients to save up their comedy programmes for the two-week wait. It really does seem to relieve the stress and helps the time to pass just that little bit quicker.

I is for Inner Voice – Stop Ruminating and Worrying, and Practise Mindfulness

Sometimes your inner voice can run away with your thoughts and theories, creating a stressful situation in your mind that just isn't there in reality.

Our inner voice can create worry, which is a misuse of our imagination and only serves to create negative outcomes. It is our brain that creates this stressful situation and this is called psychological stress – it is a stress that we have created in our mind.

151

So many of my patients worry about the result of IVF even before they've started the cycle. When you notice that you are worrying then say STOP to yourself and try to change your thoughts to positive ones. Try to focus on the moment, instead of worrying about the future – practise mindfulness.

Ruminating is another negative emotion that focuses on bad experiences that happened in the past. Some people just can't seem to get things out of their mind and become obsessed with overthinking past mistakes. Again, what has passed has passed and we can't do anything about it. Practise mindfulness to really focus on the present moment.

T is for Thank You – Be Grateful for What You Already Have in Your Life

Gratitude is a vaccine, an antibiotic and an antiseptic.
John Henry Jowett (1864–1923), Presbyterian teacher
and writer

Saying 'thank you' and being grateful for all the good things in your life has a very positive effect on the body, again by releasing those wonderful endorphins and increasing our feeling of wellbeing.

By saying thank you, we are also training our mind to think positively and it helps to put everything into perspective and to appreciate everything we do have. Be grateful for the things you have in your life, and stop worrying about the things you don't have.

By saying thank you and focusing on the good things in life, we also focus on other people and other things, and it stops the 'woe is me' attitude.

Start every day as you get out of bed by saying thank you for all the things and people in your life you are grateful for.

Y is for 'YES, I Will Be a Mum' – Believe and Trust in Yourself and Your Body

There is little difference in people, but that little difference makes a big difference. The little difference is attitude. The big difference is whether it is positive or negative.

W. Clement Stone

The power of belief is enormous. It is also called the placebo effect in medicine. If you talk to any oncologist or cancer specialist they will say that the patients who have a positive attitude to treatment and believe they will get well again quite often have a more favourable outcome than those with a negative attitude.

If you really want to be a mum and you really believe that, then one way or another you will.

I really do believe, and have seen results in my clinic to confirm, that those women who are positive and really *believe* that they will become pregnant, invariably do, while those who are negative and are constantly thinking what to do next when this IVF fails are setting themselves up for failure.

In Conclusion

Fertility problems are not always linked with emotional issues, but most often are. I hope that helping you to understand your emotions will help you unravel many of the issues such as anxiety, worry and fear that may be impeding your chances of becoming a mum.

Eating the right foods, doing a moderate amount of exercise and practising the relaxation techniques will all contribute to helping you achieve your goal. Thinking positively and practising imagery and visualisation techniques will encourage new neuronal pathways (neurogenesis) to form in your brain.

Lighten up, laugh and have fun, and don't put your life on hold – so many women postpone holidays and decline wedding invitations 'just in case' they're pregnant. Life goes on and you're more likely to conceive when you're least thinking about it. Control your inner voice and stop the worry and ruminating by practising mindfulness techniques which allow you to focus on the present moment. Be thankful and think about all the people and things around you that you're grateful for – appreciate what you already have in your life instead of fretting about the things you don't have. And above all, have a belief in yourself and your body and know that one day very soon, yes, you will become a mum.

Acknowledgements

To my dear friend Yvonne for giving me the encouragement to publish

To my patients who willingly shared their personal experiences to encourage others on their journey

To Richard and Marcus for painstakingly helping with the proof reading

To all my colleagues at CRGW who do a fantastic job

To Amy, Alice and Robert and the team at Troubador for their enormous patience and advice

Bibliography

Adam H Balen and Howard S Jacobs, *Infertility in Practice,* Churchill Livingstone, London, 2003

Alan E Beer, *Is Your Body Baby friendly?* AJR Publishing, USA, 2006

Alexander Lloyd, PhD and Ben Johnson MD, *The Healing Code,* Hodder and Stoughton, London 2011

Alice D Domar, *Conquering Infertility: Dr Alice Domar's Mind/ Body Guide to Enhancing Fertility and Coping with Infertility,* New York, 2002

Boivin J and Takefman, J E, *Stress level across stages of in vitro fertilization in subsequently pregnant and non-pregnant women.* Fertil.Steril, 1995, Oct; 64(4):802-10

Christine Northrup, *Women's Bodies, Women's Wisdom,* Bantam Dell, New York, 2006

Christopher Williams, *The fastest Way to get Pregnant Naturally,* Hyperion, New York, 2001

Colette Harris, *The PCOS Diet Book,* Thorsons, London, 2002

Daniel J Siegel, *The Mindful Therapist,* W.W. Norton & Company, New York, 2010

Daniel Kahneman, *Thinking Fast and Slow,* Penguin Books, London, 2011

Deepak Chopra, *Perfect Health,* Bantam Books, London, 2001

Deepak Chopra, *Super Brain,* Rider, UK, 2013

Domar A D, Siebel M M and Benson H. *The mind/body programme for infertility. A new behavioural treatment approach for women with infertility.* Fertil.Steril. 1990, 53:246-49

Donna Eden, Energy Medicine, Piatkus, London, 2008

Elizabeth Lee Vliet, *PCOS*, Savy Women's Guide Publishing Inc, Tucson, 2006

Emma Cannon, *The Baby Making Bible*, Rodale, London, 2010

Gary Keller and Jay Papasan, *The One Thing*, John Murray, London, 2013

Genevieve Behrend, *Attaining Your Desires*, Bottom of The Hill Publishing, USA, 2010

Geshe Kelsang Gyatso, *Eight Steps to Happiness, Tharpa Publications, Uk, 2012*

Giovanni Maciocia, *Obstetrics and Gynaecology in Chinese Medicine*, Churchill Livingston, London, 2004

Gloria Arenson, *Five Simple Steps to Emotional Healing*, Fireside, New York, 2001

Herbert Benson, *Timeless Healing*, Simon and Schuster, New York, 1997

Howard R Lewis and Martha E Lewis, *Psychosomatics* The Viking Press Inc, New York, 1972

Jack Canfield and Mark V Hanson, *Chicken Soup for the Soul*, Vermillion, London, 1999

James Schwartz, *The Mind-Body Fertility Connection*, Llewellyn Publications, Minnesota, 2008

Jean M Twenge, *The Impatient Woman's Guide to Getting Pregnant* Atria Paperback, New York, 2012

Joe Griffen and Ivan Turrell, *Human Givens*, HG Publishing, UK 2007

Joe Griffin, Ivan Tyrrell, *How to Lift Depression Fast*, HG publishing, Great Britain, 2004

John Ratey and Eric Hagerman, *Spark, How Exercise Will Improve the performance of Your Brain*, Quercus, London, 2010

John Ratey, *A User's Guide to the Brain*, Abacus, USA, 2003

Julia Indichova, *The Fertile Female*, Adell Press, 2007

Kate Brian, *The Complete Guide to IVF*, Piatkus, Great Britain, 2009

Lifang Liang, *Acupuncture and IVF* Blue Poppy Press, Boulder 2003

Marilyn Glenville, *Getting Pregnant Faster,* Kyle Cathie Ltd, London, 2008

Michael Dooley, *Fit for Fertility* Hodder and Stoughton, Great Britain, 2006

Randine Lewis, *The Infertility Cure,* Little Brown and Company, New York, 2004

Rhonda Byrne, *The Hero,* Simon and Schuster Uk Ltd, 2013

Rhonda Byrne, *The Magic* Simon and Schuster Uk Ltd 2012

Rhonda Byrne, *The Power* Simon and Schuster Uk Ltd 2010

Rhonda Byrne, *The Secret,* Simon and Schuster Uk Ltd 2006

Rick Hanson, *Hardwiring Happiness,* Rider Uk, 2013

Shawn Talbot, *The Cortisol Connection,* Hunter House, Alameda, 2007

Sidney Rosen *My Voice Will Go With You,* W.W Norton & Company Ltd, London, 1982

Sjanie Hugo, *The Fertile Body Method,* Crown House Publishing Ltd Carmarthen 2009

Susan Jeffers, *Feel the Fear and Do It Anyway,* Vermillion, London, 2007

Ted Kaptchuk, *The Web That Has No Weaver*, Rider, Uk, 2000

Valerie Anne Worwood and Julia Stonehouse, T*he Endometriosis Natural Treatment Programme*, New World Library, California, 2007

Zita West, *Zita West's Guide to Fertility and Assisted Conception,* Vermillion, London, 2010

Zita West, *Zita West's Guide to Getting Pregnant, Harper Thorsons*, London 2005